THE LAST KISS

NOT A ROMANCE

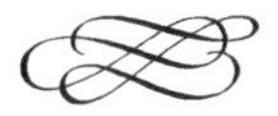

D J CATTRELL

Copyright

For any enquiries or permissions, the publisher can be contacted at djcatrell@hotmail.com

First published in the United Kingdom by: D. J. Cattrell

First Print: 2024

ISBN: 978-1-919-635286

Dedicated to all carers, paid or unpaid, be they children, adults, family, or friends.

It is a privilege to help others on their journeys.

CONTENTS

QUOTE

All the world's a stage,
And all the men and women merely players.
They have their exits and their entrances.
The job of every hospice is to keep them all smiling,
Until their final curtain.
That's my job now.

DISCLAIMER

This book chronicles the author's experiences working with aged care and disabled individuals. While the stories aim to be heartwarming and celebrate the human spirit, it's important to acknowledge the following:

- **Privacy and Confidentiality:** To protect the privacy of those we serve, all names and identifying details have been changed. The events and situations depicted may be composites of real experiences. The eight Caldicotte Principles of Confidentiality have been adhered to.
- **Specificity vs. Universality:** While striving for authenticity, certain details may be generalised to represent broader experiences within aged care and disability support.
- **Sensitivity and Respect:** The stories are shared with the utmost respect and admiration for the individuals involved.

This book is intended to be a source of inspiration and insight, offering a glimpse into the remarkable world of palliative care and disability support.

THE BEGINNING

INCOME GONE!

My wife and I had the conversation many times over in the previous twenty years that we had been together and the answer to the question she would always ask was a resounding 'no'! I did not want to retrain as a nurse I had done that, been there, got the T shirt. I did fifteen years in psychiatry in all areas of care and then did eight years looking after my mother until her death in 1999 who had contracted MS and I was done with nursing, thanks very much.

During that time, I did a BA Hons degree course in performing arts and then ran a slightly maverick touring theatre company with a couple of friends for a few years and my life moved on from nursing.

I have my own little business now distributing cooking oil to pubs, restaurants, hospitals, and schools for use in their deep fat fryers. I am my own boss and can choose my own hours and that allows me to follow my two passions of cooking and writing children's adventure books, not famous though, it's just a hobby!

So no, no thank you to going back to nursing, we had our struggles in the past, living hand to mouth at times but now I'm happy doing my thing looking after the kids as they grow up, and having time to take them to their many and varied clubs, quite a privileged place to be considering many other people's journeys through life.

I've got my own business, no pressing responsibilities, just enough to live on with one, at least, sometimes two holidays away each year, yeah, privileged. Then the virus turned up and everything turned upside down!

On the twentieth of March 2020 the then Prime Minister Boris Johnson made a speech that changed the worlds of many people, me included and as I stood in the doorway to the lounge, keeping an ear out for the cooker timer to tell me that the sourdough bread I was baking was ready, my world crumbled as the full impact of his words slowly hit me. I didn't care about his political beliefs; I just hated him from that day on! Bastard! Might seem a bit unreasonable but there you go, total Bastard!

My business, the business that I had spent years building up to the point where it was just about profitable enough to live on comfortably, the business of distributing cooking oil to pubs, clubs, restaurants, schools and other places died in his words within one minute! Bastard!

I had just bought a van and a car to the tune of fifteen thousand pounds which the business could only just afford and that only out of desperation because our car and my previous van had both died and been sent off to the scrapyard in the same week, the week before the announcement, the week before when I had committed myself to a huge rise in monthly payments from my business income, that week of hope, and then my income just disappeared before my ears. I realised in a moment that there was six hundred pounds now going out of the business each month and nothing much else coming in from the business!

This was not a comedy moment that was for sure. This is what I heard, I shall refrain from saying exactly what I said when I heard this statement from our prime minister, for now. Actually, no I won't "Bastard!"

"And above all, now we are going to defeat this disease with a huge national effort to slow the spread by reducing unnecessary social contact and I want to thank everyone for following the guidance we issued on Monday: to stay at home for seven days if you think you have the symptoms, for fourteen days if anyone in your household has either of the symptoms – a new continuous cough or a high temperature.

- To avoid pubs, bars, clubs and restaurants.
- To work from home if at all possible.
- Keep washing your hands.
- I know it has been tough.
- I know it has been inconvenient.

But these actions that we're all taking together are already helping to take the strain off our NHS.

We are telling cafes, pubs, bars and restaurants to close tonight, as soon as they reasonably can, and not open tomorrow"

Debbie looked up at me as she heard this to judge my reaction

"They will be allowed to sell takeaway food and drink" he added.

I just looked open mouthed at Debbie who was sitting on the Sofa with our girls, then back at the telly then back at Debs. "Inconvenient! Is he having a fecking giraffe?" I couldn't believe what I had just heard, and I stood there in stunned surprise, probably like millions of other people up and down the country, as he ordered all pubs, clubs, restaurants and theatres to close down from midnight, taking my income with them.

Debbie could sense this cataclysmic change in our fortunes "Might not be for long though eh? It'll probably be gone in a few weeks, this virus thing, probably, maybe?" she said, then turned the telly off. The bleeper sounded telling me to get the bread out of the oven. Our daughters went upstairs to get ready for bed and then ready to come back down for me to present them with their tea. They sensed that Daddy was presently not a happy bunny, they might have taken a tad longer to come back downstairs, I can't remember!

Too much was going on in my brain, so I went into automatic mode and got the oven gloves, whilst Debs appeared in the kitchen behind me, "Bread smells lovely, is it a sourdough?" she said cautiously.

I nodded without saying anything, I think I was in a state of shock "We'll have about a week of income whilst I collect all of the waste oil, but then I'm bust, I think." I noticed the bread already resting on the wire rack. I had got it out of the oven and slid it off the baking tray without noticing it whilst my thoughts raced, "Yes, sourdough." A bit of me was raging, a bit of me was numb, and a bit of me was planning what to do next in this sudden crisis and coming up with diddlysquat.

I loved my small business for many reasons. It meant that I was my own boss and that I was responsible to no-one except my customers. I could finish delivering cooking oil when I wanted. After all I wasn't delivering blood supplies, there was no rush. It meant that over the years, although I didn't earn much, at least I could be there for my two daughters as they grew up. Being there to take them back and forth to school, being there to take them to their clubs and there to cook for them (I love cooking almost as much as I love my kids) until Debs got back from her London job to take over and leave me to my other passion, which was writing children's books.

It allowed me time to think about stories and plotlines and different recipes that I could try out and a whole host of other stuff that I would write down when the kids were being bathed by Debbie but most of all I was independent, not well off, but independent, scraping by with just enough, but not any more. Goodbye business, goodbye independence, goodbye income. Bastard Boris!

All that was swept away by the virus and Debbie, tactful as ever said "You've got lots of strings to your bow so even if the worst comes to the worst, you still have options, don't you?"

My eyes narrowed in suspicion. "Yes, I have other options. Only last week James from the builder's yard was asking if I fancied a couple of days a week driving the forklift for him. Seems his regular driver is off to have surgery. I'll see if the offer still stands."

Debbie wasn't fooled one bit, instead she smelled the blood of defeat, of me having no choice but to retrain as a nurse so that we could survive this personal financial crisis! "Bread looks lovely darling. I love it when you bake bread, it just fills the house with that lovely aroma." She paused and leaned on the kitchen top "You could always re-train though, as a nurse. This might be just the right time."

I shook my head. "Really? You know how I feel about that, it's a past life alright, how many times? Just no! Okay?"

Debbie was not backing down though, not this time "But if the business folds, then we may not have a choice!" I smarted at the inclusive "we" bit of that sentence. She wasn't going to have to do the re-training and then take on the responsibility of being a Staff Nurse and probably running a ward with all the stress that entails.

I confess that I raised my voice more than just a little. "Just no! All right? Can we just see what happens, eh? It might only last a couple of weeks and I don't want to re-train at my age, ok? So just no!"

A moment of awkwardness blundered into the room and sat uncomfortably between us. "Let's just have dinner, shall we?" Debbie nodded, hugged me, and went to round up the kids up for dinner. I grimaced to myself, hoping that if everything did go tits up then the forklift job offer was still on the cards.

The rest of the evening was spent discussing the inevitable "what if's" and coming up with not much of a plan. We began to realise that we were okay for now as Debs worked for a bank in London as a PA which gave her a reasonable income, probably not enough for us all to live on for long. We had some savings in the bank to draw on but that wouldn't last for long either.

Then we started thinking about people living in flats with no gardens and people in rented accommodation and people who were already living on the poverty line and, well, just people really. This was not good news for anyone, but we decided to just run with it and see what happened next. After all, how long could this last, a month or two maybe. Surely once the winter was over this would all just disappear like winter flu, wouldn't it?

Two days later the Prime Minister announced the closure of all schools "Until further notice" and I remember thinking, like many of us probably remember thinking, "Well much as I love my kids, no school, really? Just pile it on, why don't you?" Total Bastard!

IN NEED OF A NEW JOB

A POSSIBLE COMPROMISE

As the days passed, we all started getting used to a new way of living that was a slow and unexpected shock to us all: kids at home 24/7 and not allowed to mingle. Yet, though we didn't know it, worse was yet to come. After a couple of weeks, the money began to dry up and I'd had to stop the music lessons for the kids, their karate lessons went in a previous cull of the family accounts, as did guides. The girls took it fairly well at first as the money and options melted away, but later after a few months they would become more restless and resentful of the whole Covid thing.

Still, on the upside I got to walk our slightly overweight dog a lot more and for a lot further, much to her benefit. When I came home there was gardening and cooking to keep me sort of occupied. I love cooking, even on a shoestring, but the money was most definitely running out. I was getting worried. Household bills were beginning to go unpaid while toilet rolls were disappearing from shops at an alarming rate, as was bread flour, I mean bread flour for goodness' sake!

I had made our own bread for years... don't get me started on supermarket bread because I would go on but safe to say that home-made is easier than you think and much tastier. Bread flour shortages?

I had visions of thousands of domestic cupboards across the country being stacked up with panic-bought product that might never be used, despite the fact that our supermarkets themselves never actually seemed to run out of actual bread! The world was becoming a very weird place.

Then one day, the day, I was mowing the front lawn and musing on those issues. Were people learning to make bread en-masse or would there one day be a glut of bread flour making its way into the recycling bins like a slow dusty tsunami? Then the hammer fell.

You know that feeling when someone tells you something that you know is right, but you just don't want to hear it.

"Hi Jas, how's it going? Debbie tells me that you're looking for work. Have you thought about retraining?" Gertie walked up the road to our house with her usual smiley face and gentle swagger. I stopped mowing, knowing that I was in for a chat, she was after all Irish and in my experience Irish people don't do small talk: they do long talk.

Gertie was a General Nurse who worked at the local hospice. Our kids had grown up together, going to the same school and playing together in the same street. Gertie, and her husband Grahame were the closest thing to family that we had in our neighbourhood and their New Year's Eve parties were legendary around our way, but this was a conversation that I didn't really want to have. "I'm too old to retrain, possum and I'm done with nursing. I'm an oilman now, though you wouldn't think it would you. My van hasn't moved out in over a fortnight!"

We stopped and chatted about the girls and how they were taking the whole thing. Gertie's eldest had been furloughed and her youngest was doing the same as our eldest... not much... and we had a good moan about home schooling. "You're right," she said. "It's all a bit crap, but it is what it is. By the way..." Oh yes, I thought, here it comes... "If you don't want to re-train the OW are looking for Health Care Assistants, bank staff and to be honest, they're a bit desperate. You'd be doing them a favour if you applied."

Now that was something I hadn't thought about and to be honest, I raised a curious eyebrow. My beef with retraining was that it would come with a shed load of responsibility and paperwork, online training; and after years of working for myself and having no responsibilities to any bosses, retraining was a definite no.

I had been promoted to being a Charge Nurse thirty years before and ended up mostly sitting in an office and going to meetings; not my thing really, nature of promotion I suppose but I became a nurse in order to nurse people, not to be a manager. Not sure I'd be a good manager now to be honest, I have grown an irreverent streak over the years. Having said that I am in awe of the managers at the Hospice that I work for. You'll see why later because they manage this amazing team that I sort of joined, no spoilers.

But working as a Health Care Assistant, well that was like going back to what I enjoyed doing when I started nursing as a teenager: looking after patients. "I'll give it some thought Gertie" I said, "What's the pay like?" I said jokingly.

She smiled "Standard: You won't get rich, but you'll be able to pay the milk bill and you'd be great at it, really you would!"

I smiled to myself about the pay "Nothing changes then" I said. "I still don't think it's my thing, but thanks for thinking of me. I'm probably better on a forklift than in a ward these days. What's the OW anyway?"

Gertie smiled "It's the outside ward; you'd be nursing patients in the last two weeks of their lives… you know, those who choose to die at home, you'd be great at it. Really."

I'm not sure what the expression on my face was but part of me was horrified at the idea! Surely that was a specialist thing by itself, a thing you had to train for. And I said as much. "That surely needs some training I'm guessing; sounds a bit intense? The last two weeks of people dying at home do you mean?"

Gertie laughed out loud. I guess she had that kind of reaction from many people who weren't familiar with palliative care. "There's a week's induction course that's been cut down to three days. That's how desperate for staff they are. There are more nurses off with Covid or self-isolating than there are out there in the field and with your history you'd be a shoo-in!"

GERTIE'S TESTIMONIAL

I have been asked many times why I work in palliative care. I often hear "you must get used to it." I remember a former colleague said to me that working in palliative care is like marmite you either love it and stay like I have, or you can't do it and leave.

To me it's a vocation and a privilege to be with patients and their families at this most poignant time. I have met so many amazing people in my role – I sometimes feel that I am not worthy to be in their presence from the way they deal with their experiences from courage and strength. I have seen grace, dignity and beauty within suffering. These people have taught me so much about life which has moulded me into the person I am. Also, the day I get used to it is the day I will leave. Without compassion and humility in our hearts, we are nothing.

IN NEED OF A NEW JOB

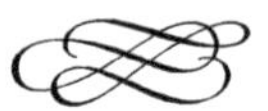

PART II

Debbie had clocked Gertie from the house and came out to say a socially distanced hello. My heart sank a little as Gertie started their conversation with, "I was just telling Jason that the Hospice are looking for HCAs; just a few days training and you hit the ground running. They're desperate for the right people right now and Jason ticks all the right boxes don't you think?"

Debbie looked at me with that look, the look that she had when she knew she had me cornered but what she said to Gertie was "Oh really, what's an HCA?"

Gertie looked at me but smiled at Debbie "Oh you know. They used to call them Nursing Assistants or Carers, Health care assistant. It's a community job and they're a bit desperate for staff."

As you know by now Debbie had wanted me to go back into nursing for some time. I have no Nurses pension to look forward to as I'd spent it when looking after my own mum and Debbie had a habit of dropping monumental hints about how I would be so good as a Nurse and how my personality was so suitable for Nursing and how much I would enjoy being a Nurse again and, and etc, etc, blah, blah, blah!

I turned the mower back on, drowning out any further conversation and shouted out over the noise of it "Just going to do the back lawn." Then I pushed the mower round to the back of the house knowing that Gertie was essentially giving Debbie ammunition for a "why not?" conversation later in the evening. I spent the next hour or so in the garden tending plants, watering and rehearsing reasons, and probably very plausible excuses, as to why going back into nursing would be a really bad idea, despite, not having a job or an income, etc.

I knew in my heart of hearts that I was done with nursing, and this was defo not going to happen. I'd been cleaning bodily exudations off people since I was fourteen years old and then when I left the profession it continued with cleaning up my dear old Mum for the following eight years and to be fair, I was ok with all that but during that time and despite having bugger all money, I had somehow still ended up with a horse to look after which came with, you guessed it, more poo picking!

I know it's a bit random, but I spent the next twenty years literally muck picking out of various fields and on top of that, successive girlfriends and relatives had palmed off their unwanted dogs to the extent that I ended up having five dogs, a horse, and an ailing Mum to look after. I had done my time dealing with other creatures' bodily exudations thank you very much!

Inexplicably, two days later I found myself having a phone job interview with the Hospice for the position of HCA for the Outside Ward with a very nice lady asking me why I thought that I might be suitable for this position and frankly I was at a bit of a loss for a reply. Even as I had been twenty-five minutes earlier when my eldest daughter handed me the phone with a slightly smug look on her face that had somehow been passed down to her by her mother, (the smug look that is, not the phone.) I was still wondering how the hell I had been talked into this!

At the end of the interview the lady confirmed with me that the training for the job for which I had just been accepted was going to be a shortened three-day course due to the Covid situation and that social distancing would probably not be possible owing to the nature of the job. The course would include Manual Handling and various aspects of care appropriate to End of Life (EOL) care in the community. Clearly, they were having a staffing crisis and were in desperate need of bank staff to fill the gap. Bank staff are not permanent staff that do overtime. Bank staff are those carers, nurses etc who are employed to fill in the gaps when there are not even enough permanent staff to fill the overtime roles.

The job was to see to people who had decided to die at home in what was expected to be the last two weeks of their lives and I was seriously doubtful if I was the right person for that kind of job. I'm an easy banter, joking along with sort of a guy not a serious, intense giver of hope to a hopeless situation person so I had some very serious doubts about how I would fit into such a role.

I did the course the following week and I was pleasantly surprised about how much things had moved on from twenty-five years ago. For one thing the Australian lift which was performed by having a nurse stand on either side of the bed bending down, hooking the patient under the armpits, and dragging them up the bed, had fallen out of favour. There was a new revolution in lifting bed bound patients up the bed called a slide sheet.

The slide sheet is revolutionary in moving patients up the bed. It is a tubular made from a very strong nylon that can be placed under a patient and then the patient can be easily slid up the bed. It must have saved thousands of hours lost to the NHS in back injuries.

Not only that, but patients were expected to move themselves around or must be subjected to an Occupational Therapist assessment to see how they could best be moved with as little danger of injury to the nurse or patient as possible. The world of nursing that I had known as a teenager had become seriously more professional!

The job that I had signed up to now operated a two-shift system: four hours for four patients in the morning to help people in the community who had elected to die at home to start their day, and four hours in the evening assisting them to settle for the night. That seemed entirely logical to me at the time.

We had four aims apparently, which were, to keep the patients pain free, agitation free and anxiety free; and to support their relatives as much as we could. To be honest that sounded ok to me: I'm fairly chatty, confident and gregarious if you catch me on the right day so, yeah, I could probably do that, possibly, maybe?

I told Debbie that I would do two days, two days only and see how I felt about it. I had done the training course and I had done a shadowing shift. It was a bit weird, and I wasn't prepared for what was to come, but who could be, despite the training? That was it though, no expectations. I would do two days and then decide one way or the other because frankly there were other jobs out there that were less involved, less intense and which probably paid better. Two days in the last two weeks of people's lives, okay, let's see how that goes.

NO BREATHING AND GRAVY

FIRST DAY, FIRST VISIT

I woke much earlier than I usually would and put on a pair of trousers (I'd worn jeans for fifteen years!) and my new uniform tunic, drank coffee, ate toast, did the usual ablutions, checked the handover with the addresses of the patients that we had to visit and then headed out to the car and made sure that I could get the Hospice email on my phone so I could note the postcodes. Debbie caught me at the door having already been at her computer for twenty minutes (obsessive compulsive workaholic that she was!) to give me a good luck hug for the day.

I looked down at her (she is much taller in personality than height to be fair). "Two days okay, I'll give it two days but to be honest darling you know how I feel about this."

She nodded and smiled up at me. "You're giving it a go and I'm proud of you." I rolled my eyes, returned her kiss then headed off to my first call wondering what on earth I had let myself in for.

I pulled up into the road at 07.55 and Amelia, my partner carer was already there in her car waiting for me even though I was early. This was my first patient, and I was more than a bit nervous, but calm. I'm fifty-eight years old and fairly well travelled in life experience, yet this was an area of care that was entirely new to me, and I didn't want to look like a completely inexperienced novice. I have often suffered from imposter syndrome. Obviously though, they had put me with someone who was experienced and knew the ropes, hadn't they? Of course, they had, hadn't they?

Amelia got out of her car and started masking up. She had a plastic apron hanging out of her uniform pocket and was already wearing a pair of blue plastic gloves. It all seemed a bit surreal at first as I began to don the same kit from the back of my car.

"I'm Amelia, nice to be working with you. Have you been here before? This one's new to me, she's eighty-two and she only has days. You're quite an experienced nurse though I hear. I've got my notepad out to take some lessons." She joked expectantly.

AMELIA'S TESTIMONIAL

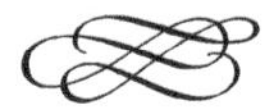

After caring for my daughter for nine years, all the support I got from the hospital, etc was amazing. The nurse we had with us till the end gave us so much support and she made me think about end of life. It's such a rewarding job and a privilege to have families want us in their house at such a sad time. To know we all make such a difference to their days makes me smile.

NO BREATHING, NO GRAVY

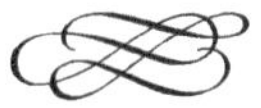

PART II

My brain went colourful with sparks of self-doubt bursting out as I processed that bit of info! Yes, I had done a shadowing shift to get an idea of what to expect as an HCA; and yes, I had been a nurse in psychiatry but that was thirty years ago or more. But suddenly I was feeling like I had just jumped with no arm bands into the deep end of a swimming pool and the swimming instructor was asking me how to swim!

I bumbled. "Well, I, this is my first patient to be honest and I haven't been in nursing since forever really, so if it's ok, I'll take my lead from you because you probably know more about what you're doing than I do and um …."

She looked surprised and I cringed inside myself thinking that she's going to think I'm an idiot; I had a full-on imposter syndrome moment. "You'll be fine," she said reassuringly, and she gave me a conspiratorial smile. "Let's go in and see what we see, eh?" Then she gave me a friendly grin. I needed that!

Amelia had a slight stigma in one eye giving her that pretty Barbara Streisand look and an Essex accent that would have given her an easy place on 'Love Island' had she been just a tad younger (not saying how many years younger though!) and I warmed to her easy manner immediately. She opened the gate, and we walked up the drive, I felt a need to reassure her that I wasn't a complete numpty. "I haven't done nursing for thirty years so while I have nursing experience it was some time ago. This stuff is all new to me. How about you?"

Then my nervousness and sanity were reassured by her answer. "Been working for the Hospice for years, babe, and mostly in the Community. I'm enjoying it more than I thought I would when I first started. You'll be fine, don't worry. It's like riding a bike is nursing, isn't it?" With that offhand statement she released a mental safety bomb into my fragile world, and I started to calm down a bit.

One thing I learned from my days as a psychiatric nurse was ironically never show your fear, or indeed your true feelings in a crisis, and I have often felt that is a useful universal skill for anybody dealing with the public from supermarket staff to waitresses and waiters.

You can't show what you're actually thinking as you are providing a service and people using that service don't see a person, they see a persona: a waitress, a nurse, a checkout assistant, all whom in their view are trying to frustrate them rather than help them. I think we all fall into that trap sometimes, and sometimes we, including the person serving us, just forget that we are all just humans really.

We reached the back door of the house. "The notes said to just knock and go in Shall we?" she said. Not waiting for an answer, she knocked and opened the door "Hello. Anyone around?"

As we walked in through the back door into the kitchen a lady in her early 60s came towards us from the lounge smiling. I took the situation by the horns, saying "I'm Jason and this is Amelia". Then I smiled at Amelia, waiting for her to take the lead.

"I'm Annie, Jenny's daughter." the lady said "She's had a quiet night but to be honest I'm surprised that she's still here. It's been like this for the last week or so: she hasn't passed any fluids but then she hasn't drunk anything in ages either. We thought she'd been gone days ago but she's a tough old bird is my Mum and she's from Yorkshire too, so that'll tell you something, eh?"

I looked at Amelia, probably wide-eyed and expectant, hoping that she would say something wise and sensible. She didn't disappoint. "That's not unusual Annie. How's her breathing? Yorkshire air builds strong lungs for sure. Have you got the bowl and flannels somewhere?"

And there I was. Having been delivering cooking oil to pubs and clubs, hospitals, and schools for the last fifteen years in a world of chef's banter, sweary, oily yards and the quietness of driving around through the countryside with no real responsibilities except to bring home the bacon as it were (apologies to vegetarians there: maybe to bring home the harvest) here I was in a world that was utterly new to me.

I realised immediately that I had a lot to learn and the people that I was going to learn from were those who were standing right in front of me: The hospice carer that I was with and the relative who was the main carer and daughter; and also of course the patient whom I was about to meet.

Annie showed me into Jenny's room and there she lay in the profiling bed, 82 years old and as fragile looking as a glass mouse. Her breathing was very shallow, her mouth open and her frailty very evident. Her eyes were closed, and I could see the pulse in her neck as she had lost so much weight through her cancer. Then Annie said. "She used to be so strong my Mum; looked after us all as kids on no money at all. Never in my days did I ever expect to see her like this. Here, the controls are on this side of the bed." She passed me the bed controls.

Profiling beds were a new thing to me. They work on hydraulics which allows them to rise up so that we as nurses, can work with the patient at hip height. When I was a nurse thirty-five years ago profiling beds hadn't been introduced. Instead, you had to get a knee down onto the bed, hook a patient under their arms and hoik them up the bed until their head hit the pillow. Not easy, not dignified and definitely not good for anyone's backs.

These hydraulically controlled beds can lift a bed-ridden patient up from behind their shoulders and up from under the knees, making the whole business of moving patients around their bed so much easier than before as does the slide sheet more of which later. I was beginning to feel like a dinosaur in new clothing! I looked at the profiling bed controls that Annie had given me and pressed a self-explanatory button that showed a picture of an arrow pointing up.

Amelia came into the room with a washing-up bowl full of hot water as Annie handed her the towels. I had understood from my shadowing shift that relatives were asked to provide a bowl for us to use (usually a plastic washing-up bowl) along with two flannels and two towels. One light-coloured flannel and one dark-coloured: basically, light for hands and face and a dark one for downstairs. It saved us getting confused as to which flannel was supposed to wash which bits. I'm not sure about you but in our house, we have a flannel each that just does everything but when someone is bed-ridden downstairs can get messy.

Annie left the room and I looked at Amelia "I'm new to this so I'll take your lead if that's ok. You're the expert here." I was on the wall side of the bed and Amelia was on the door side.

I think she could tell that whilst I might sound confident, I might be bluffing. I was indeed a bit nervous for after all here was a lady in her eighties, barely breathing, and yet in need of being washed so that she wouldn't develop bed sores and so that she could be left as comfortable as we could make her without tearing her paper-thin skin.

Without saying anything Amelia immersed the flannel in the bowl of water and wrung it out. Then she so gently wiped around Jenny's forehead saying "I'm just going to give your face a wash if that's ok Jenny?" and she told Jenny exactly what she was going to do before she did it and she did that for everything that we did for her. That was a good lesson for me. She washed Jenny with such an exemplary gentle care whilst Jenny responded not at all.

Then she immersed the flannel back into the water again and gave it to me saying "Hands next."

I took the flannel and lifted Jenny's hand that was on my side of the bed. It was cold and so I let the wrapped flannel linger for a moment or two on her hand to warm it then passed it back to Amelia who in turn gave me a hand towel and a tub of cream. I dried Jenny's hand gently then massaged a blob of cream into her hand and arm. It's necessary to do this because lying in bed all day and night can make your skin dry and itchy especially on your back and cream really helps.

It's also important for different reasons. Creaming down a patient's arms, legs, back and shoulders is a physical connection, a massage if you like, a way of saying that you are not alone, and we care for you even if you can't respond to us.

Sometimes when someone appears to be unresponsive the only response you get is when applying cream or warming their hands.

We finished upstairs and then needed to check her pad downstairs because although she was catheterised, we still needed to make sure that she hadn't opened her bowels. If she had, we would have to clean her there as well. It was also an opportunity to wash and cream her back so that even though she was not very responsive at least we could be sure that in her last days she didn't have an itchy back or bottom or any visible sores.

Then it happened. After we had finished washing her front bottom and creaming it, she stopped breathing. I looked over to Amelia thinking to myself "Surely I'm not going to be laying out someone on my first visit." Amelia looked back at me with the same thought as Annie reappeared at the door, saw her mother not breathing and looked at us both in turn as we looked back at her. A moment or two passed and God knows what was going through all our minds right then.

That momentary pregnant pause filled the room and we waited, me with eyebrows raised and looking down at Jenny, sensing the inevitable. More seconds passed and just as it seemed that this was indeed the end, this was it, this was the moment I was sure, even I couldn't hold my breath for this long so defo. Jenny a sharp intake of breath. We then all let out breaths that we had all been holding; my brain plumed colours in relief!

Annie rolled her eyes and growled "She's been doing that for days! I just never know if that's her last breath or not!" She was tearful and frustrated. "Every time it happens, I just want to fling my arms around her for our last goodbye and then she springs back to life!" She clearly didn't want her mother to die but neither did she want her to live in an endless limbo either.

Annie was worn out with this emotional uncertainty and her shoulders were sunk. I looked at Amelia and turned to Jenny. "When was the last time you had a drink or something to eat Annie?" I asked.

Annie looked surprised at the question "Well, I, I can't, I mean it's been so, um."

I looked up at her "Sorry to ask Annie and I know we've just met, and you seem to have been doing this for a while, but may I ask, is there anyone else helping you to look after your mum?" This was a question that came easily to my mind as I had looked after my own mum for years until she died, but I'd had a great deal of family support and amazing help from her carers. I also knew that I had been lucky to have the family that I had at the time I needed them.

She looked a bit confused. "Well, no, not really. Dad passed away five years ago and I'm an only child." She shook her head "'Only child' seems like a strange thing to say at my age." She shook her head again "I have help from Anna next door; she helps with the shopping and stuff when I can't get out but other than that, it's just been Mum and me really."

I smiled at her because here I was on safe ground here "Any chance of a cuppa? Sorry to ask but my kids ran me ragged earlier and I haven't had a drink for hours. I take one sugar in tea or coffee if you don't mind?"

Amelia turned, looked at me and her eyes wrinkled ever so slightly in understanding, then at Jenny who said, "No sugar and white either way please."

Annie nodded, looked at her mother and then nodded again. "Right, tea? I'll go and do that then." She left the room with a confused sense of purpose.

I looked over Jenny at Amelia "So what's next then boss?" I said 'boss' specifically to remind her that I was a novice at this in the hope that she would take the lead and that I wouldn't look too much like a floundering idiot.

She smiled back at me and took a breath. "It's time for the slide sheet now so that we can slide her back up the bed. Sort her pillows out and wash behind." Then, although Jenny still showed no signs of consciousness Amelia said to her in a soft, caring voice "Jenny, we're just going to roll you to face Jason so that I can get this sheet under you, is that okay?" Jenny obviously didn't respond but Amelia kept talking and reassuring her as we worked to make her more comfortable, washing her back after we had rolled her, checking her pad and applying cream. There, in that moment on my first visit, I got an inkling of how amazing the team members that I might be joining were and that this could be just the beginning of my journey with them. Amelia just chatted away, showing me what to do and letting the seemingly unconscious Jenny know what we were going to do next at every turn.

I learned a huge amount on my first visit that day. Most importantly, I learned the routine that all the OW nurses followed, though as yet I still had to make that routine stick in my head. Work from top then front, then legs and then back and bottom, then slide sheet tucked under and pad to follow as I find myself saying even now.

When we had finished clearing up and Jenny was looking more comfortable (and thankfully breathing more regularly), we went back into the kitchen to find Annie pottering around, pointlessly cleaning up an already immaculate kitchen. She smiled as we walked in. "How is she?" Amelia smiled back "She's ok now, I think. Pads dry, no bed sores and she doesn't seem to be in any pain. She seems settled enough for now."

Annie handed her a cup of tea and Amelia took it gratefully, dropped her mask and sipped. "Oh, that's a nice cuppa! We don't often get a drink on our rounds Annie. Thank you. I have to say that you're doing an amazing job of looking after your Mum. You must be so tired! Do you get a break other than the occasional help you get from your neighbour?"

Annie just shook her head. "Not really, but I don't mind. There's only me now that my husband moved away. To be fair, I was glad to see him go! Had to be there for my mum though because as she often said, she brought us up on a piece of bread and a passing cloud and she was like that, was our mum. So, I owe our mum." Tears were welling in her eyes.

I took my cup from her and asked, "So what did you do before you ended up looking after Mum and Dad?" A part of me just knew that she had been there for her Mum whilst her Dad was on his way out and a part of me knew that she just wanted someone to talk at. I say at because as we all do, she wanted to be heard. I could feel it and she didn't disappoint.

We spent the next twenty minutes nodding and empathising and smiling at her stories of how her life had been abroad when she was younger and how she and her husband had parted way before she came home to look after Mum and Dad. She had given up a lot to be there for them and I was truly touched by that. Like many of the people I was to meet over the coming months I was just amazed at her devotion to those closest to her; and for her, that was her Mum and Dad.

My first visit dropped me in the deep end emotionally, and I was glad of it. Amelia taught me the basic ropes of being an HCA for the OW, caring for the physical needs of people who had maybe two weeks left to live; and both Amelia and Annie taught me of the role the HCA's had in comforting the relatives of those others who were on their way out of this world, the real carers. Never be in a rush, always take time to listen to the relatives because they often need as much care as the patients do, sometimes more.

Then we were off to our next patient, ten minutes' drive away and a yet world away from my first OW experience.

I followed Amelia to our next patient. We had four visits that morning which was the general routine. Four visits per shift's were with an hour allocated for each patient. The morning shift was generally the longest as, just as in a hospital ward, the focus was on a full body wash, emptying catheter bags and recording the relevant amount of urine passed. Noting if the patient had opened their bowels during the night and checking for any changes in the patient's condition that might be of concern.

Our next patient though was the opposite of what I had just experienced with Jenny. In fact, our next patient was seriously grumpy and quite deaf. As we alighted from our vehicles Amelia and I masked up and put gloves and flimsy (almost pointlessly so) plastic aprons in our uniform tunic pockets with two sets of Nitrile examination gloves, rubber gloves that are an essential part of personal protective clothing that shall be forever known as PPE. Always need to carry a spare pair. At that time in the development of the pandemic no-one really took masking up that seriously, but we did it anyway. Only in later months would the daily death toll in the country show us how important masks were. And then only months after that did we discover how useless they were if you didn't have the right ones.

In my book, those little blue medical masks are about as much use as waving a hanky in front of your face and praying to the God of avoidance. A good FFP3 that totally seals the breathing area from nose and mouth with a strong filter mask and tight goggles are what is needed instead.

FIRST DAY, SECOND VISIT

NO GRAVY

Amelia and I approached the neat and tidy little bungalow together and I asked, "The notes say that he is non-ambulant but that's about all I've got. Have you been to this one before?"

Amelia hesitated before ringing the doorbell. "No, he's another new one. CA Mets with underlying issues. Not sure what to expect really. He's Stan and she's Janine." Then she grinned at me. "Shall we?" I wondered to myself if this was what it was going to be like doing this kind of work: deal with what you get presented with and roll with the punches.

I also guessed that CA Mets was probably a description of a primary cancer with metastases, metastases being bits of the original cancer that break off and are transported around to other areas of the body, causing secondary problems. But made a note to look that up on the net later. I knew some of the jargon of general nursing but not much of the detail.

This was just my second visit, but I figured it couldn't possibly be any more moving or scary than the first one and I was right. It was way weirder!

We were greeted by a very well-dressed lady in her mid-eighties and as she opened the door she said "I don't think that he needs you this morning but do come in." The bungalow was very tidy, well looked after. It was engulfed in ornaments and other dust collectors as well as an extensive collection of artworks adorning the walls. She ushered us into the lounge.

Amelia said, "So I'm Amelia and this is Jason. How was Stan's night, and how are you?" I noted that "and how are you?" question and filed it. In the OW the relatives were definitely part of the equation, part of the whole picture as I was becoming to understand only too well.

Yes, the Outside Ward carers were there to make sure that the patients' physical and mental needs were taken care of in their last two weeks of life, but the ladies on the ground, the ladies I would get to know and be a part of as a visiting team member, they knew that the relatives needed as much care as the patients in the bed, or in this case, not in the bed did and that was instinctual knowledge born of experience in the field of end of life care.

The lady before us was dressed very demurely and I think I would describe her as well-spoken, a bit posh "The old Duffer's on the toilet at the moment but I'm expecting an appearance imminently. Would either of you care for a drink. He's not been too bad last night. The physio was in yesterday and told him not to shuffle when he walks. I don't know why he's taken to doing that, the old fool."

Then we heard Stan shouting from the toilet. "Why have you changed the gravy. What have you done to it? It don't taste the same."

Janine rolled her eyes and shouted back at him "The nurses from the Hospice are here Stan." She looked at us both "He's deaf as a post, you'll have to shout to be heard by him."

Stan shouted back "What?" and he seemed to be coming closer.

Janine shook her head and turned to us "It'll take him a moment or two to get here. I've got tea, coffee or Prosecco, I prefer the Prosecco myself." She picked up a well-charged glass and smiled at us. This was a morning visit after all and each to their own. I'm fifty-eight and enjoy I a drink probably too often myself so I'm never going to judge. Besides, at my age I get that everyone has their own stories and gremlins.

I smiled at Janine. "I'm waiting for beer o'clock when I get home after the second shift thanks" I turned to Amelia with a raised eyebrow.

Amelia caught my look and said "I'm good thanks. Just had a cuppa. I thought Stan was non-ambulant?"

Janine smiled politely, "If only. He was off his pins for a while but he seems to be picking up a bit. Can't keep an old rogue like him down for long!"

Then Stan emerged from the Bungalow corridor wielding a Zimmer frame, wearing pyjamas and what looked more like a smoking jacket than a dressing gown. He looked me directly in the eye, paused whilst he looked me up and down, then shouted out "She's changed the bloody gravy for Christ's sake! The gravy!" Then turned to his wife "The gravy's not the same. Doesn't taste right!"

Janine ignored him "These are the nurses from the Hospice Darling; they're here to help you" She rather shouted more than said. Then turned to us. "Deaf as a bloody post!" and rolled eyes.

Stan then looked us both up and down. "I don't need no help!" then he paused and shouted "Just get her to make the bloody gravy properly. Can't have a steak pie without a proper gravy can yer!"

It wasn't rocket science. Amelia and I realised that we had just walked into a row and that Stan was probably not within our remit. Chances are he would be heading off to the Social care arm of the relevant service within the next day or so. Walking, talking, and arguing with his wife, he looked very much like he had more than two weeks left to live. But as I later discovered people can go down really quickly. Amelia smiled and shouted at Stan, "Are you sure that there's nothing that we can do for you this morning that isn't gravy related, Stan?"

Stan smiled broadly and shouted back "No, I'm fine thanks." Then he looked at his wife. "Not unless you can find me a better cook!" He carried on with his journey, past the main lounge and heading slowly to a small room with a comfy chair and his own TV. Janine clenched her fists in frustration.

I looked at her and she was obviously more hurt than she should be by that offhand comment and something familiar struck me. When I first moved into the family home ago to look after my mum twenty-eight years ago, I remembered that the water tasted weird. I had the Water Board come out to test the water as I was convinced that somehow it was contaminated. The water was fine. It turned out that the antibiotics that I was on for a chest infection had affected my taste buds.

Janine turned a little dramatically, to go into the kitchen, obviously more than a little hurt. "Janine. Has Stan had his medication changed lately?" I asked.

She stopped short and turned back to me, hesitated for a moment. "He's got another urine infection. As if liver cancer wasn't enough!" Then she got a little angry, "And just for his information I have made his bloody gravy from the same recipe for fifty years!" This time she was talking in a pointless stage whisper.

I was beginning to like this job. I was feeling a bit useful "I think that maybe his medication is affecting his taste buds. It's probably nothing to do with your cooking."

She stopped and looked at me. "That's a thing that can happen? Oh, I never knew that. I thought he was losing the plot to be honest."

From somewhere in the corridor came the response "I heard that you old nag and I'm as sane now as the day I married you." he paused "Mind you when I put it like that...."

Janine ignored him but smiled at us. "Are you sure you wouldn't like a drink? I'm about to break open the Chateau neuf-du-Pape." She said hoping to keep us there, more for company than need and, I felt that she would probably be having a nap after her lunch-time gravy-making.

Amelia shook her head "Thanks but we're fine. If you have any worries though, you make sure to ring the central point number. They are there 24 / 7. Okay?"

Janine nodded "I love the old goat really but don't ever tell him that, eh?"

Stan's voice boomed out from the corridor "I heard that too. Got a hearing aid, y'know."

As we stepped outside, I took off my mask and said to Amelia with a big smile on my face, "Why are we here? I don't think that Stan is on his way out just yet, is he?"

Amelia shook her head "Not really, but it happens sometimes. They're at death's door when they're referred to us and by the time, we get to them we find that they've perked up. Sadly, it won't be long for Stan though, don't be fooled: his cancer is spreading rapidly apparently." This was definitely a new world to me.

FIRST DAY, THIRD VISIT

STRESS PERSONIFIED

"Who do you want to do next?" I asked Amelia. The next two patients were both seven miles away but close to each other.

Amelia looked at the list on her phone. "We'll do Ray next and then Mabel. Ray is very end of life, and his poor son Ed seems so stressed bless him. You'll love Ed: he's totally devoted to his dad."

Obviously, I was curious. "Has Ed got any other support such as family helping etc?"

Amelia smiled at me. "He has lots of support, especially from his older brother but he's looked after his dad for five years and now it's coming to the end. Ed moved in with him when Ray's first round of cancer hit and has been looking after him ever since. Ray's daughter-in- law is a carer and she's been helping out a lot lately. Mind you, there's a lot of tension in that family; they don't all get on with each other. Whilst the elder brother, James I think his name is, is helping Ed and he's a great support, the other brother is very critical and keeps asking how long Ray has left and when does the will get read. Luckily, he's away for a few days."

I nodded wondering what "the tension in the family" meant but didn't enquire further. As a former psychiatric nurse and psychotherapist, I was well aware of the depth and breadth such a statement might imply and how complicated family dynamics could become. The other brother was obviously a little cold to his father's plight but who knew what the past had been like for him or the rest of the family?

Sometimes we forget ourselves and judge others unfairly There are focal points in time when events bring more stress to families than is usual, such as relationship breakdowns; your kids getting married; your kids saying "No" to you for the first time and getting away with it; births, deaths or even just moving; house but I was guessing that in palliative care the tensions at those points would be running higher in some families than in others. Though the brother still sounded as though he might be a bit of an arse, everyone has their own story and as I say it's not fair to judge anyone without knowing the full facts.

We pulled up and "alighted" from our vehicles. I feel like I'm stealing that word back from police reports. Awesome! Parking was easy on this visit but that would not always be the case as I was to discover later.

We togged up and knocked on the door. Ed appeared and let us in through the kitchen. In all my years in psychiatry I could not have been offered a better example of someone holding back a tidal wave of stressed-out emotions. Ed could barely stand still. He looked down at the floor and then up at Amelia repeatedly. She asked in a matter-of-fact way, "Not a good day then Ed?"

Ed shook his head and from the way he did it I sensed that Ed was slightly different to the rest of us, and I still don't know how he was different. I gave up on labels years ago, but Ed was different. "Not good, no." he said, "Not a good day." His fists scrunched and then opened again whilst he talked.

Amelia was still putting on her gloves. "I haven't seen you for a couple of days my lovely." she let her eyes smile from behind the mask. Obviously, she had a fondness for Ed, a fondness born out of empathy. "I hear Dad's not so well," she said, tying her plastic apron on.

Ed picked up his mobile phone from the kitchen table. "Not so well, yes. Dad's not so well. Dad's not been drinking." He ran his hand through his hair. "Not eaten for ages either."

Amelia pushed him gently through the kitchen and into the lounge where Ray was. I looked at our next patient and knew exactly what was going on here. Ray had just days left for sure, maybe only hours. He was emaciated, inert and his breathing was extremely shallow and a little bubbly.

When went into to the lounge, Ed walked back and forth around the room looking at us and then looking away from us in equal measure, saying very little whilst holding on to his mobile. I asked where the bowl was, and Ed pointed to the door we had just come from. "Through the Kitchen and turn left before you reach the back door."

I smiled back at him. "Okay, thanks. Nice kitchen by the way." Ed looked at me with a brief moment of curiosity. "I'm Jason." I said and then walked off to get the bowl whilst Amelia pulled Ray's notes from the green folder that contained all the notes on him from the Hospice including those from the registered nurses and others. She scanned the notes and as I walked back in with hot water and flannels I asked, "Ray hasn't eaten anything or drunk anything for couple of days then, Ed?"

Ed ran his fingers through his hair and walked around in circles "No, nothing, nothing. He can't even swallow anymore." He clenched his fists not I thought in anger but in frustration and then he looked out of the window almost as if he didn't want to look at the immediate future, at his Dad's immediate future.

I put the bowl down on a stool beside the bed and looked down at Ray. Amelia had raised the bed up so that we could work at hip height. Just by looking at the man you could tell that he had lost a ton of weight through his illness: sunken eyes, loose skin, and a sense of fragility. His head lay on one side and his tongue protruded slightly.

I put a towel under Rays face as best I could, dropped a flannel into the water, squeezed it out and began to wipe Ray's forehead and cheeks as gently as I could, telling him everything that I was going to do before I did it, as Amelia had done with our previous patient Jenny, regardless of the fact that he was entirely unresponsive. He lay there, all skin and bone, and I dried his face by softly dabbing it with the towel and while Amelia looked on.

She could tell that I was re-learning on the job old skills that I hadn't used for years. Maybe nursing is really like riding a bike: it had become sort of instinctual in me over the years. Amelia smiled reassuringly at me whilst Ed paced around the room. Then she turned her attention to him. "Have you eaten today, Ed?"

Ed looked at her in a little surprise "Um, no not really. I don't think so?"

Amelia nodded "You've got to take care of yourself as well as your Dad Ed. We've talked about this." Ed looked down as if he'd just been told off and he looked utterly miserable. Then Amelia looked at me and said, "You alright for a few moments Jason?"

I looked at Ed and then at Amelia. "Yeah, no worries. If I need you, I'll call. You can supervise me from the kitchen door if you like. boss." I would need her when the time came to roll Ray so that we could check for sores and incontinence. The latter was not impossible but nothing in, nothing out as it were.

Physical contact wasn't strictly allowed then because of the virus, but still Amelia put her arm through Ed's, Although they were roughly the same age, she said, "Come on kid, let's see what you have in the fridge shall we?" Ed nodded and they left the room together to find him something to eat.

I washed and dried Ray's hands, face and chest and applied creams; then rolled up the duvet and washed his legs and checked his heels for sores. Bed sores are not uncommon in bedridden patients as I knew from looking after my own Mum. Profiling beds with their air mattresses are amazing at preventing bed sores but you still have to be careful.

The air mattress on the bed is very cool and I was to later discover why. Imagine a Lilo and then imagine that the air in one of its tubes goes down and then re-inflates very slowly, and that each tube does this at a different time creating a sort of very slow ripple effect across the bed. That relieves pressure from a different area of the body on a continuous basis while the continuous air circulation helps to keep the mattress cool. Whoever invented that saved a lot of people a lot of pain, whoever invented it is a universal hero!

I finished washing Rays legs and his heels were ok apart from a little redness for which I applied a cream called 'Derma S'. There are several creams on the market that do a similar thing now. When I was nursing thirty plus years ago it was simple: we had Sudocreme and that was it. Most of us know Sudocreme as a nappy cream though we used it for everything from nappy rash to grazes and spot cream for teenagers. One tub seemed to last for centuries.

In the intervening years, I discovered that the range of creams one could use had exploded and I was going to take the time to find out what they all did. Some were for softening skin; some were for hardening skin; some had antibiotic properties; and some were barrier creams to stop soft skin from becoming softer because of wetness from other sources. The list of creams has become almost endless but their uses are generally three-fold.

Barrier creams, these are aimed at preventing wetness from other sources getting to the skin and it works by providing protection and avoiding degradation of the skin.

Emollients are used to soften dry / flaky skin whatever its cause.

Medical uses like antibiotic, steroid and antifungal creams are used to alleviate infections and fungal infections of the skin.

Other creams are mainly used for beauty and anti-ageing purposes whatever their manufacturers claims. I once listened to a skin specialist on Radio 4 (yeah, I know!) who said that the best anti-aging creams are actually high factor sunblock creams because there are three main causes of ageing skin, internal causes such as drinking, smoking, drug-taking; long-term illnesses and genetics; and external causes: essentially the sun. She said a little petroleum jelly around the eyes was just as good as the most expensive anti-aging creams.

Having said that, I know that most of my female friends love a good pampering with all sorts of treatments. And why not? If it makes you feel good go for it! Having said that as well, I know that men are increasingly well into skin care and why not? Whatever floats your boat, eh?

My old man was a coalman and I've been an oilman for a while now and how you might look or feel really doesn't enter into the job for us, but everyone is different, and history tells us that from the Aztecs and Egyptians to the French courts of Louis the 14th, skincare and make up have always been a thing. Not my thing though. I'll go straight for the face lift when the time comes!

Amelia came back into the room with Ed who was holding a plate with a something sandwich on it in one hand and a drink in his other hand. Amelia pointed to a chair in a motherly but forthright way she said, "Sit down and eat and don't get up until you've finished, right?"

Ed was a grown man of about forty years of age, but he sat down as asked. He looked a bit sheepish. "Right, sorry."

Amelia smiled at him. "Don't be sorry, you numpty, just remember that you are as important as your Dad ok?" She looked at me and rolled her eyes and then back at Ed as she moved round the bed to help me roll Ray. "Is your brother coming round soon Ed and where are the girls?"

Ed's older brother, James had been supporting him more for the last few months as Ray had got worse. Ed took a slurp of his drink to clear his mouth. "Yes, James will be back soon; he had a job to take care of, but he'll be back soon. Babs took the girls out to get supplies I think; they'll be back soon too. Babs is very good with Dad; she's very efficient, I think." Then he took another bite of his sandwich and chewed it slowly, keeping his eyes on us.

Lots of people would have come in and out of his and Ray's house over the last few months and all would have different levels of caring. I knew that from my own experiences with the carers who looked after my own Mum, so I got that he wanted to keep an eye on us. I also got that he deferred to Amelia and obviously trusted her completely. He didn't know me though, so he kept an eye on me.

We rolled Ray together, washing him down and applying creams where necessary. Amelia went slower than I think she usually would have just to make sure that Ray actually ate his sandwich and drank his drink. "Babs is Ray's daughter-in-law; she's also a carer like us but she works in Temperlies Care home. You know, the one by the cinema, you know the one?" I nodded "She's been really helpful to Ed just lately, hasn't she, eh Ed?" Ed chewed and nodded. Amelia leaned forward to me and said, "Lovely girl and she's been washing the bits that Ed doesn't like to wash, if you know what I mean." She pointed downstairs and mouthed "the foreskin".

I looked at her for a moment and then said quietly "It can be difficult to take the hat off your Dad's head as it were and wash it I reckon; it must weird him out a bit. Good on Babs, eh?" Amelia nodded.

Just as we had finished, James burst into the house like a whirlwind carrying a shopping bag which he dropped on the side and went straight to Ray asking as he went "How's he doing, do you think Amelia? I know we shouldn't ask but the old boy's not looking good is he. How long do you think?" Then Ed caught his attention "You made a sandwich Ed. Good for you; about time you ate something!" Ed stopped chewing and looked at me for some reason. "Amelia made me do it. Sorry!" I just nodded an "it's fine, it's okay" sort of nod back to him.

James smiled at his brother then went and sat down next to him "That wasn't a criticism ya twit! You need to eat." He turned to Amelia. "By the way, I emptied 100 ml from the bag earlier. Not much is it?" I assumed he was talking about the catheter bag.

Amelia finished up by lowering the bed and clicking on its brakes. Then she walked towards the kitchen and out of Rays earshot. She whispered to James who joined her. "You know that I can't say James, but usually when we get to this stage, it could be hours, could be days, but probably no more than that. By the way the bin's full. Have you got a bag for our rubbish?"

James shrugged "Yeah of course, I hope for Ed's sake it's not long." We went into the kitchen proper to write up the notes in the green folder. James provided a bag into which we put our disposable aprons and gloves. We had to keep our masks on until we left the property though. James was at pains to thank us. "We all think that you folks are amazing by the way. Thank you, Amelia, and your new bloke?"

I was a bit rabbit in headlights again just at that moment watching how Amelia had been so amazing with the family. It was like she was almost family to them "Sorry, I'm Jason," I said. "They employ me to do the heavy lifting" I was feeling like a bit of an intruder.

He laughed "Yeah right, Jason. Seriously you're all amazing. I know Ed is stressed out, but he has taken the brunt of all this." He turned to Ed. "You're an amazing brother bruv." And then he turned back to Amelia "Thanks for getting him to eat something. We've been trying but his entire focus is on Dad as you know. He's a bit OCD but he has been amazing with Ray these last few years." That's obsessive-compulsive disorder. I told you I'd keep you up to date with the acronyms.

Amelia smiled back at James and Ed. "No worries. It's probably the uniform but it's what we do." Then she spoke directly to Ed. "It will be hard when Ray goes Ed, but you've been his best friend and you should be so proud of yourself as I've told you before lots of times. It's hard I know Ed, but Ray loves you, doesn't he?"

Ed nodded, James smiled at us and as we left I felt a range of emotions that I find difficult to describe. To be honest, by now I was a little emotionally drained on my first shift. But we had one last visit: Mabel.

I can't remember what went through my head on the car journey to our next patient but what I did know was that this was personal nursing on a level that I had never experienced before. I was an absolute novice here, but I was also utterly intrigued by it. I understood that these were amazing and caring people who specialised in end-of-Life Care and that for some families they were like family.

For over fifteen years, I had run my own business during that time I had obviously spent a lot of time talking with many chefs and other people in the hospitality industry, I had sort of worked in my own bubble, responsible only to myself. This one morning shift had sort of blown all that self-isolation away completely. Here I was, in a job that was all about everybody else's lives and nothing to do with mine.

It was an amazing day that I was going to unpick later, but not later that day. At the time, I was just taking it all in without knowing that was what I was doing, I was just at the beginning. I had trained in the institutional care of patients, whereas now, well now I was discovering deeply personal care.

FIRST DAY, FOURTH VISIT

THE UNWINDING CLOCK

We pulled into a cul-de-sac for our last patient visit of the morning. We alighted from our vehicles. Note that I am now owning that word. Amelia pulled aprons and gloves from the back of her car whilst telling me "Mabel is unbelievable; did you read the handover on her? Ninety-eight years old and still trundling to the lounge and back. She has definitely been going down a bit this week, but she is still such a force!"

I stuffed more gloves and an apron into my pocket whilst asking, "About that though, I didn't see any sort of diagnosis. What's the brief?"

Amelia stopped for a moment and looked at me with a smile. "She has nothing wrong with her Jason; she's just old and slowing down to a stop like a clock at the last unwind. She can still make it to the bathroom though. Well, she could yesterday at least."

Amelia was around twenty or more years younger than me but as I looked at her gloving up, I felt quite junior to her. She was obviously very experienced in her job, and I briefly wondered what it must be like to work in the IPU (In patient unit) where she'd come from.

But I kept the off the cuff analogy in my mind because for some lucky people death really was just a gentle end to a life lived. I would come to realise that for some death was less about focusing on the progression of a particular disease or condition but actually more about approaching the finishing line. I thought that over the next few days, I might see Mabel reach her finishing line very slowly.

I was to realise all that later, but right now I had no clear idea how to interpret her decline. I was guessing that she was just very old. I wasn't entirely a novice in this area having grown up in the old people's homes that my mother ran as a Matron. She would call us down to educate us by getting us to help out.

I helped her lay out my first corpse when I was about fourteen years old, and I just sort of took that as normal without thinking too much about it. Looking back, it was an odd childhood. I had helped pull up so many over-washed stockings on to old ladies' legs that when my mates were all drooling over girls in stockings, a part of me would wonder just how many washes those flimsies that were the object of their attention would take before you had to tie a knot in the top of them to stop them falling down. As I say, an odd childhood.

They did everything very differently back then of course but that same day that I helped lay out a corpse and I had called bingo in the main lounge for the residents when a 94-year-old man had shouted out at the top of his voice "Fuck yes, Bingo!" He shocked the whole place. He grinned a sorry to everyone, but let's face it, a win is a win! When I look back at my life now it does all seem a bit weird, but I wouldn't have it any other way.

As a fourteen-year-old I had giggled at an old man swearing because obviously adults were not supposed to swear so it was funny. Now though I realise that whatever your age every moment of life is hard, challenging, and confusing so when you get a win, live in the moment, and own it! No spoilers, but one of the patients in this story really brought that home to me, she gave me her last kiss. Live in the moment.

As at the time of writing a fifty-nine-year-old bloke and now a Hospice HCA (Bank staff), I have come to realise, looking back that other kids probably didn't have that kind of fun in their childhoods....

ıaying out a corpse and then giggling at a sweary old man playing Bingo. I feel for them all and how they missed out.

Anyway, we rang the bell, togged up and waited for her daughter Brandy to open the door. I asked Amelia as we stood on the doorstep 'Is her daughter really called Brandy? I hope her surname isn't Snap!"

Amelia laughed. "Yes, she is, but her surname is Midwinter and she's a love, trust me." Then she looked over to the neighbour's door. "The man next door has dementia and doesn't seem to have much support. He keeps hassling Brandy and Mabel. It's not in the Handover notes for some reason but Mabel's younger and fitter sister Fran is also here looking after Mabel. Actually, this is Fran and Mabel's house."

The door opened and a lady of around 60 years of age ushered us in with a smile. I've got to be honest here because I was taken aback by just how pretty this lady was. She reminded me of my eleven-year-old daughter who is skinny as a rake and who has beautiful brown eyes that will stand her in good stead with any future suitors, I've got the shotgun ready though!

Brandy looks were as striking as Joanna Lumley or Julia Roberts's. Yet in her smile lay an easy manner and an easy welcome. "Mum had a full wash down last night as she had a little accident." She said to Amelia. Then looked at me "And you are?"

I did my best to smile without turning back into a schoolboy After all, I'm a happily (very happily) married man but sometimes when you meet someone as pretty as Brandy you are a little thrown off balance! "Jason. My name is Jason" I looked at Amelia whilst speaking to Brandy. "I'm just coming back into nursing after a break. How's your Mum?"

Brandy looked a little concerned. "To be truthful, I'm a little worried about her. Come on in now." She ushered us into the hallway and within three steps I could see Mabel in a profiling bed off to the left in the first room in the bungalow. Brandy looked at her sleeping mother "She's really struggling to get to the bathroom at the moment. Aunt Fran and I really had to keep her up on her Zimmer frame last night just so that we could wash her."

Amelia stepped in. “So shall we see how she is, then maybe we can get her up and out of bed for a short while?”

Fran called out from the lounge “Is that the carers? Hope they have better luck with her than we did last night.”

Amelia shouted back, “Hi Fran, it’s Amelia, I have Jason with me. He’s new but he’s good with the heavy lifting apparently!” She grinned mischievously at me. “We’ll just go in and say hello for now, eh?”

We walked into Mabel’s bedroom and all three of us stood around her bed. I watched and waited for Amelia’s lead. She stroked Mabel’s forehead, then her cheek. “Hello Mabel, Wakey, Wakey,” she said softly, “It’s Amelia. How are you doing?”

Mabel woke slowly. “I’m ok I think, what? Sorry?” she said in one slow sentence.

Amelia put her hand on Mabel’s. “We’ve come to get you up for the day and give you a little wash-down. Is that okay?”

Mabel smiled. “Yes dear,” she said slowly. Then she said, as she turned to look at me through slightly bleary eyes and trying to focus “Who’s this?”

I couldn’t help but smile back at her as she had her daughters’ beautiful brown eyes, just like my daughter’s. “I’m Jason, Mabel. Just another pair of hands to help out if that’s ok with you?”

Mabel smiled and spoke slowly. “Thank you, Jason. Yes, it’s lovely to have a little help these days.”

Fran appeared at the door of the bedroom that used to be a lounge. “If you could get her to take her teeth out and give them a bit of a scrub that would be very helpful Amelia. She hasn’t had them out in days, and I worry as you know, don’t want her getting thrush, do we?” Oral thrush is a fungal infection often found in babies and older people. It’s easily treated but not nice to have.

Amelia was already helping Mabel to stand by placing a Zimmer frame by her bed and encouraging her with soft low tones. I moved to Mabel’s other side to assist, she said to Fran, “Yes, of course. Mouth care is always a little tricky at times.” Then Amelia turned back to Mabel “Can we refresh your teeth today, Mabel? I find everything tastes so much better after a denture scrub.”

I looked at Amelia in utter astonishment. I mean, she was twenty years my junior and she really didn't look like she had false teeth. It must have been an amazing dentist to have done that job on her teeth because they looked so perfect. I have come to love Amelia to bits over the past year or so, but at that moment her teeth didn't look like false teeth.

Mabel looked at Amelia and narrowed her eyes in suspicion. Then smiled broadly in forgiveness at Amelia's lie. "Yes Amelia" she said whilst standing and starting her slow and epic journey to the bathroom with her Zimmer frame. "We can do that today." Amelia smiled at the shared lie. I learned another two important lessons. Amelia's teeth were clearly her own and that some lies are worth sharing. And the smile was worth sharing too.

We helped Mabel to the bathroom and to do her ablutions which were completed at the speed of a snail doing maths. We then helped her into the lounge to sit in her favourite chair. It was just as well that she was our last morning client because the travelling between the two rooms alone took a good half-an-hour with a sit down on a hallway seat halfway. Mabel refused a wheelchair. Amelia told me later that Mabel thought that wheelchairs should be reserved for ill people!

When Mabel was settled in for the day Amelia, asked me to write up the notes. Suddenly I was somewhat at sea. It had been a while since I had done that. Writing up the notes is essentially describing what you have done at that visit adding any important extra information about the patient on something that was very familiar to me called continuation sheets.

It's worth spending a moment on explaining continuation sheets as while they can be laborious, they are also hugely important for several reasons. Firstly and obviously, they let the next shift know what it was important to note on your visit: sores to be aware of; whether or not someone was, let's say, a bit backed up in the bottom area and needing some assistance, or how they were just doing in general so that any deterioration could be noted and anything that needed to be done by the next shift wasn't overlooked. Information such as "more responsive this evening" or "200ml passed in catheter bag, bag not emptied." A catheter bag can hold 1000 ml of urine so sometimes changing it every shift would be pointless if someone is hardly drinking then the rate at which they pass urine decreases.

Writing up the continuation sheets is very different from doing a handover. The continuation sheets stay in the client's home where they can be read by the relatives and is a record of what has happened during each visit.

The handover, recorded securely online between staff might include more confidential information and warnings such as "Husband reports finding things very tough at the moment and may require a sensitive approach" or "Patient quite distressed and wife suffering from dementia. Please ask S/N to assess care needs." Or "Large friendly Alsatian in house." I always carry dog treats, a trick I learned from our postie. Information in the handover is more functional and informative for the following shift.

So, I checked out the previous entries in the notes and just added what came next and what we had done. Apparently, the previous night Mabel had been exhausted by visiting relatives. I should have attended to this on our arrival perhaps, but Brandy had been so articulate about her mother's needs that it hadn't been necessary. It had made me think that this nursing malarkey was slowly coming back to me slowly My nursing instincts were being re-awoken after all these years. It was weird but actually, and against what I thought was my better judgement, I was quite enjoying it.

Once I finished the notes I went back into the lounge with Amelia and went to say goodbye to Mabel, but she was already asleep in her chair a snoring softly. Brandy looked at her with and evident love and devotion in her eyes. "She gets so tired so quickly now. She's barely eating these last few days."

Amelia asked: "Is she having trouble swallowing at all?" and she sat down on an armchair, which was a bit of a surprise to me because I thought that we were done here.

Both Fran and Brandy sat down on the sofa. "We know that she hasn't got forever but we're not quite sure what and how quickly it will happen," said Brandy.

From behind her mask Amelia gave a sweet smile that leaked through into her eyes. "Brandy, we really can't say but shall we go into the kitchen and have a chat?" She clearly didn't want to talk in front of Mabel even if she was asleep and it was equally clear that she was going Fran and Brandy up to speed but diplomatically. "Would you keep an eye on Mabel please, Jason?" I nodded and sat down on a chair next to Mabel.

Brandy looked at Fran, Fran nodded back to her and they both stood and went into the kitchen to talk about what the next few stages were possibly going to look like. All caring and lovely, but I was left there sitting on my own like a prune not really knowing what to do next.

I didn't know these ladies as well as Amelia did, so I just stayed sitting on the chair next to Mabel. I picked up the aforementioned green folder and reviewed what I had written down in the notes. "Full care given; no sores evident; Mabel still continent and able to assist in personal care, ambulant but very tired" Not much really, so when I was done, I looked out of the window for a while and listened to her breathing and light snoring.

They had a lovely garden: well-tended and full of colour. I love a good garden and spent a while admiring the look of it and the attention that it had clearly had.

There was a veg patch with an array of cucumbers, courgette plants, tomatoes and so much more. Just my sort of garden, really. Time passed and I started to wonder if I should get up and pop into the kitchen which is what intended to do, but as I stood up Mabel unexpectedly opened her eyes and said "Lovely, my garden isn't it?"

I looked at her in some surprise "I thought you were asleep Mabel: sorry if I woke you. Yes, you have a beautiful garden. I love a pretty garden me."

She smiled slowly up at me. "They worry about me dying don't they Jason, [no flies on this lady for sure!] but I'm not worried, Jason. I don't mind dying, I've had a good life." I was in no man's land there for a moment, so I waited for her to speak again.

I sat back down next to her, and I took off my gloves to write but she put her hand out to me, a stranger to her, and so I took it, despite Covid regulations. "I'm sad for them" She continued "because I won't be here to comfort them, I won't be here to hold them when I go. but that's the way of it and they'll be fine eventually." Then she looked back to the garden. "I don't think that I'll last as long as the cauliflowers
will I?"

I looked at her and shook my head. The cauliflowers were just seedlings and a few months off being ready to be harvested. I was seriously put on the spot by her, but I couldn't lie to this lovely old lady. "Sorry Mabel but I think you might be right."

From absolutely nowhere, I got hit by a rush of emotions and stemmed a tear as the meaning of her words and mine unfolded in my mind; and I squeezed her hand, as I realised the moment, we were both in. "If your sister and daughter are anything like you Mabel, I think they'll definitely be fine; and yes, they seem to love you very much." We both sat there for a moment, strangers holding hands and looking out into the garden, and I thought about my own Mum. "I was sad when I lost my Mum and they'll be sad too when they lose you, I'm sure." This was proving to be the strangest morning that I had experienced in years, perhaps ever.

She squeezed my hand back and said, "I think so too. I'm tired now Jason. It was nice to meet you." She looked into my eyes, smiled the last smile that I would see her smile and said "I'm tired now; I might just have a nap" then without another word she slipped her hand from mine and dropped back off to sleep.

Suddenly my heart was in my mouth, and I was like a rabbit in headlights again. I was going to find that feeling, the being in headlights feeling, was going to be a bit of a regular thing in this job. Amelia and the others reappeared at the door. Fran said "Oh good, she's asleep. She didn't have the best night last night so hopefully she'll rest a bit now. I just wish she could talk to us a bit more.

I just looked at Fran with my mind in a bit of a weird whirl thinking "Well she was able to talk to me just now" but instead said "Yeah, she did just wake up for a few moments there whilst you were all in the kitchen." They all looked at me expectantly and I didn't really know what to say or even whether Mabel was actually asleep sitting in her chair. "She said that she loves her garden. It is definitely a lovely garden you have there."

They all looked at me in a pausing moment, working out the implications of what I had just said. Then Fran broke the moment. "She designed every inch of that garden. It's been her obsession for years: digging away, planting flowers and veggie things. Not my cup of tea really. Brandy keeps the lawn nice though don't you love?"

Brandy nodded and turned to Amelia whilst I looked at the possibly sleeping Mabel not really knowing what to make of my brief exchange with her. I would of course be back in the afternoon or evening with Amelia to help her into her nightie and get her back into bed when Mabel might or might not be a bit more alert. To be honest, this was just new territory to me.

Amelia stripped off her apron and squashed it into her gloves: a neat trick that I now use. "We'll be back this afternoon, Brandy. but I'm not sure what time but probably between 7 or 8 pm if that's okay?"

Whilst being drop dead gorgeous and in her late fifties or early sixties (I'm no expert on age) Brandy also had a serious gravitas about her. "Of course, that's ok Amelia, you've both been amazing. You just take all the weight off our shoulders, don't they Fran?"

Fran agreed wholeheartedly and here on my last visit of the first morning, I was beginning to get a sense of the kind of work that I was getting into. I've got to be honest here: I hadn't enjoyed four hours of working so much in over twenty years. Don't get me wrong, I love my little business, but the sheer variety of the people I had just met along with amazing competence and care was quite a lot for to take in. What a roller coaster of a morning!

Outside I chatted with Amelia by our cars about the morning and I asked if it was always like this. She thought for a while and said "Yes, it is, I think. So how did you like your first shift?"

I couldn't help but smile. "Yeah, it was ok. Is it you and me again this afternoon?"

Amelia shook her head. "No, I'm off now for a couple of days at last! We've been right under it since this Covid thing kicked off, short staffed like you wouldn't believe. This is my fourteenth shift in a row. I'm off home to relax!"

I de-masked and asked, "Oh right. What are you up to tonight, then?"

Amelia looked shocked. "Well, ain't you a fast mover?"

I blinked then reviewed what I had just said. "No, what I meant was …."

Then she laughed and said, "Only pulling your leg Jase. I'm having a Prosecco party with my girls. Got my first night off in fourteen shifts, so it's a party night for sure. I'm glad you turned up as bank staff or I might have had another fourteen without a break! Bloody Covid!"

She opened her car door matter of factly and said, "You're with Sally this afternoon, my usual partner in crime. We call her "The head mistress". she'll tell you off for something or other without a doubt as she can be quite stern. We all love her to bits, though. She's one of the best of us. Have fun. It's been lovely working with you, Jason. I'll do the Handover; you do it next time." Then she got in her car inexplicably singing "Sweet Caroline" and she drove off with a cheery little smile, leaving me with a sudden bout of a nervousness that I had not felt since I was a very green nursing assistant at the age of seventeen. The head mistress!

I couldn't remember I had never been more scared of and yet more in love with any nursing assistant since Jean Brown. I was seventeen at the time and she was around sixty. She was scarier than any Charge Nurse or Matron, yet she was like a mother to me. She taught me the ropes of nursing, whilst always telling me off, always being on my side and always having a spare fag for me back then (I smoked back then!) She was a Glaswegian matriarch, a seasoned Nursing Assistant and even now I am proud to say, my first proper mentor and friend in nursing. For me, she put the word "caring" into nursing in a way that no training I've ever had since has. Until now.

Head mistress, eh? I got into my motor, sat for a moment thinking about the whole morning and then drove home wondering what awaited me in the afternoon.

I was yet to meet the rest of the OW team. I was to discover that not one of them would be any less caring and competent and loving at helping relatives and patients through this most difficult part of the journey that we all in our own way take, than Amelia had been. Each of them would have a very different personality and each would be very special in their own right.

I was yet to discover that this was a side of nursing that I had never experienced in all my years in psychiatric nursing. But I also learnt that to be able to give small comforts at this critical time of other people's lives was going to prove occasionally challenging but mostly addictive... and in some cases even, dare I say it, magical. This was the end of my first shift, the first of possibly many more about which I was still undecided, still not sure what I was letting myself in for.

THE AFTERNOON SHIFT

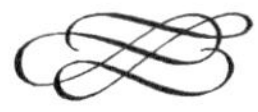

I went home that morning just before midday and as I walked in, Debbie was standing there waiting "So, how was your first shift? I've made you a sandwich."

I wasn't quite sure what to say. Brilliant? Weird? Exhilarating? Instead, I plumped for "I need a coffee" because I didn't want to hear the inevitable "Told you so". Then I washed my hands, despite having covered them it seemed in hand gel every five minutes during the day, sat down at my writer's desk and ate my sandwich whilst telling my her about the morning and everything that had happened.

It is has been a habit of mine throughout my life, if I can to take a midday nap, each day, but just for a half an hour. That day I lay down on my bed and dropped off completely. Debbie woke me an hour-and-a-half later, saying "You might want to get ready for your next shift darling: you need to leave in half-an-hour."

I woke up sharp and shocked. I never sleep for that long. Clearly, the morning had been more of an emotionally draining event than I had realised. I'm telling you this in retrospect: at the time I was just dealing with whatever came up next. I got up, grabbed a coffee and checked the emailed handover notes for any changes. Unsurprisingly Stan was not on the list. He had been shuffled over to Ravenscare but there was a new patient. I guessed that we were going to see all the patients we had seen in the morning and in the same order but with one exception. My phone pinged with a short text message from Sally, the headmistress. "We're working together this afternoon, Jason. We'll start at Jenny's."

Blimey. A bit brisk I thought. I texted back "No worries. I look forward to meeting you." Nothing came back from her to that text, no "Me too" or anything like that, which made me even more nervous.

Debbie had made me a bottle of sparkling water with me. To reduce our plastic waste, we use SodaStream for our drinking water. We use that for our water and just refilling bottles as required.

To be honest, in my mind we should all do what we can to avoid destroying the environment though of course it's the big industrial companies that can make a bigger impact. We hear a lot about the fight against climate change. Though we consumers do our bit, it's the big industrial companies who are messing up the planet. It's them, the super-rich and governments who need to sort that stuff out. (Hey it's my book. I can have a rant if I like!)

So, if I was going to be working with someone as strict as the head mistress, I would probably need to think in terms of falling back on fizzy water in the evening rather than the usual beer.

I checked the handover and looked up the first postcode into my phone before sliding (just trying "sliding" out!) into my car. The phone told me that I was going to be two minutes late for my first visit and that made me frown. I am fairly confident, but I am a bit fearful of mature Health Care Assistant's (Or Nursing Assistants as they were called in my day.) because the really experienced ones could be more knowledgeable than the Student Nurses for sure and quite often the Staff nurses too.

Many of you reading this will be familiar with the question "Do you want to speak to the person in charge or the person who knows what's going on?" The fact that everyone called Sally the head mistress definitely gave me the feeling that she was probably a ground floor person who knew what was going on, I felt another anxiety poke. I would hate to look like a novice at my age and yet I sort of knew that I was going to feel like a novice at my age.

I arrived precisely two minutes late at Jenny's house but thankfully Sally hadn't arrived. I breathed a sigh of relief and went to the boot of my car to get togged up with my personal protective equipment. Just as I finished stuffing the apron into my tunic, a little white car drew up next to me and a mature lady of a certain age rolled down her window. "You Jason?" Sally had an East London accent that clearly brooked no fools.

SALLY'S TESTIMONIAL

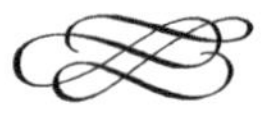

The reason I love working for this Hospice and this team are because they care and because they take their time to make it right for everyone they care for.

I witnessed care being "done" to a friend and it upset me that they seemed to rush their care or miss a few things out if they were tight on time; they never talked to them, talked over them.

Our Hospice is not a timed service. We involve family and patients in all conversations, and we are able to give them the care they all deserve to help them through a difficult time for the whole family. I wanted, from seeing how my friend was treated, to make sure that I could help to make sure others were treated better than that and that is what I really hope I do, and I won't put up with less than it being right for them.

THE AFTERNOON SHIFT

VERY UNEXPECTED FLIRTING!

I smiled my most winning smile. "Yes, indeed. You must be Sally?" She looked quite cross. She said nothing but rolled her window up and parked down the road.

She alighted from her vehicle (I'm so owning that word now!) We met at the back gate, and I asked, "Have you been to Jenny before?"

Sally barely looked at me and my anxiety levels rose a notch "Yes, she's a bit of a yo-yo this one." Then she smiled at me which was even more unnerving. "Your first day I hear: and you used to be a Charge Nurse somewhere back in time. Well let's see, shall we?" The smile disappeared and she marched to the back door where Annie was already waiting. I followed nervously, wanting to say, "Yes but that was thirty years ago. I don't really know what I'm even doing here now. Don't hurt me!" But I didn't.

Annie smiled a much friendlier smile at me and said, "Hello again Jason. She's changed since this morning." Sally looked back at me with a frown like I was a bit of an intruder on her patch. She might just have been waiting to see what I said but my paranoia was totally kicking in.

Then she turned to Sally "Nice to see you again, Sally. I managed to get some of that Derma-S cream you talked about. It's in the box of creams now."

Sally nodded and gave Annie a much more relaxed smile than I had got from her, that was for sure. "It's a good one and it should help." She said, then she came out with Outside Ward opener. "Have you eaten today, my lovely? You've got to remember to look after yourself Y'know. If you haven't, then now's a good time. Whilst me and Jason take care of Jenny and get her ready for the night. Okay?" She sounded very much like a mum, maybe even a kindly grandmother, and not at all like a headmistress when she to Annie.

Annie smiled at her. "Yes, I bought some pot noodles" Sally raised a disapproving eyebrow. "I'm kidding" Annie smiled. "I've got a lasagne baking and some broccoli steaming."

Sally smiled back and then she looked at me with what I interpreted as a slightly challenging look. "You remember where the bowl is from this morning do you?" Suddenly, she looked every inch the headmistress again!

I nodded slowly and said nothing but headed to the bathroom to fill the bowl with hot water and a touch of shower gel. Then I took it straight into Jenny's room under the watchful and somewhat distrusting eye of the headmistress. I was beginning to understand why they called her that. Yet there was something about her that was completely focussed on the people in front of us. Something almost motherly. Something totally competent and caring.

I put the bowl on the same stool that I had used in the morning and Sally immediately said, "She needs to eat properly, does that one. Easy to neglect themselves when they are the only carers." And she was right. But then she said, "You need to put a towel under that bowl. You don't want to leave a water mark on that nice stool, do you now?" she said as she looked me dead in the eye.

I looked at her and something was forming in my mind that was threatening to come out without my wanting it to it didn't. Instead, I said "No, you're right; good call."

She stood on one side of the bed, and I stood on the other. I picked the bowl up slowly not taking my eyes from hers; it felt very much like we were somehow playing a Mexican stand off scene in a black-and-white movie. I almost expected her to reach down into her tunic and pull out a Colt 45.

I slowly placed a towel under the bowl then stood up straight. With furrowed brows I looked her in the eye. In a dark and deep, slightly challenging voice I said, "I have always found that in situations like this there can only be one boss, one person to take charge: the most senior and experienced one person should lead."

She almost leaned forward as her eyes narrowed and I could feel the tumbleweed rolling across Jenny's bed. There was a tense pause as we eyeballed each other. Then I smiled innocently and said lightly, "So, as the one with the greater experience in this field Sally, would you be the boss please? I think I have a lot to learn, and Amelia told me that you're the best one to learn from."

Sally stopped. If her eyes could have narrowed any further, they would have closed. And then it happened, She smiled a proper, lovely, friendly smile and the relief went down to my boots. She nodded a little tersely at me, but it was a sunshine-from-behind-the-clouds smile "Let's start at the top shall we and we'll find out how good you are."

I smiled back at her then turned to Jenny. My jaw dropped. She lay there with her eyes open, looking at me; She said in a very weak voice that had a broad Yorkshire accent: "You're the best man in the room you are Jason."

My jaw nearly fell off! I looked down to see Jenny smiling weakly up at me. This was the same lady who had been barely breathing this morning and now she was flirting with me. "I'm the only man in the room Jenny. Nice to see that you've perked up since this morning. Is it ok for us to give your face a wash and freshen you up for the night?"

Jenny gave me a weak smile "That would be nice Jason, thank you." She said though her voice was very croaky. I could see why Annie was stressed out. To be honest, at our morning visit I wasn't sure myself that Jenny would make it through the day and yet here she was, 85 years old and flirting with me! Then she turned very slowly to Sally. "The cream is nice Sally, quite soothing; Annie put some on this morning after Amelia and Jason had gone."

I dipped the flannel in the soapy water and gently wiped her face and then Sally dried it. Sally responded to Jenny's compliment. "It's a good cream Jenny, but if I find a better one, I'll let you know." She took the flannel that I had dipped back into the hot water, wrapped Jenny's hand in it, then slowly massaged between her fingers. "Your hands are cold today, Jenny." I could tell that the warmth of the flannel gave Jenny a great deal of pleasure... as did the warmth in Sally's voice.

I was definitely learning on the job. It was through Sally then and on other visits later, that I began to reinforce my

understanding that we weren't just there to make someone physically comfortable, we were there to share their last moments and to give as much of those little moments of joy and comfort as we could both to the patient and to the relatives.

Jenny smiled slowly, yet as I looked on it was clear that whilst she was rallying from time to time, she really didn't have long. As I looked at Sally massaging Jenny's fingers as well as the concentration on her face as she did so, I could also see that just giving that small amount of physical and emotional pleasure to a lady who hadn't got long to live was what made Sally who she was.

As I reflect on the visit to Jenny, I realise that I tears of joy and empathy in my eyes; almost feeling that flannel around my own hands. I saw how special that connection, both physical and emotional was between Sally and Jenny

I was to see Sally make that connection with so many people in the future, people who are first and foremost people.

It was what made all the ladies of the OW so special. Sally might have been a bit formidable; scary even as a HCA but in the following years that I worked with her from time to time she was also the one that I would come to regard as my second big sister. I had respect for Sally from day one and to this day, she is still both awesome and a still a bit scary! We don't tell each other what we are doing during a shift: she tells me what we're doing; and I'm absolutely fine with that.

Anyway, after chatting to them for a while, we left Annie and Jenny knowing that there were only days or hours left for them to be together. We walked to our cars, "Who next boss?" I asked with a sort of a wry, collusional smile like as if we had just become mates through a shared experience.

Sally though, clocked my attempt at collusional instead she became very business-like again. I sighed to myself. Sally was Sally after all. "We're picking up a Gent from the other team tonight. Very EOL." She pulled at her car door handle which came off in her hand. She looked at the handle and then at me "Bloody car! Bloody garage!" she said very crossly. "This was supposed to have been fixed the last time it went in for repairs!" she looked at me. "What am I going to do with this? I've got the rest of the round still to do!"

I looked at her and the car with a blank mind and then I said, because I've had to do it in the past: "You'll have to climb in from the other side, I guess. You'll be able to open the door from the inside to get out, but each time you want to get in again, you'll have to do it from the other side until you can get it fixed."

She looked at me with those steely blue eyes of hers and the crinkle of crow's feet re-appeared at their corners. At our age, those crow's feet are a sign of well-deserved past smiles. "You're not as green as you're cabbage-looking are you?" she said, going around to the other side of her little car.

I smiled back at her: "Been around the block a few times with vehicles, Sally. I could never afford new ones, so I've got used to make do and mend over the years. How about I follow you to our next appointment so that if anything else falls off, I'll be able to give you a lift."

She nodded as she opened the door on the other side of her car. "That garage is in for a proper bloody chat tomorrow I can tell you," she said as she went and I immediately felt a bit sorry for whatever mechanic would come into her line of fire the next day. "I'll see you there." she said. But then stopped and said, "This is your first day so

I'd better warn: you this next one's a bit..." she paused, look down "... difficult to navigate." She looked down for another moment and, from my past experience as a psychotherapist, I understood that looking down usually signifies that we're accessing the emotional parts of our minds. "I'll explain when we get there," she said. I just nodded and got back into my car, wondering what to expect next.

FIRST DAY. SECOND PM VISIT

FOUR GENERATIONS WITH ONE LEAVING

Within twenty minutes, we had both pulled into the private driveway of a medium-to-large country house. I had passed this house many times in the past delivering cooking oil to a nearby pub but had paid it no attention as it was set back behind a hedge, hidden from passing drivers.

I had however, noticed the complex of buildings across the road from this house that housed people with special needs, and which was constantly advertising for staff. I had often wondered through the lean times of my cooking oil distribution business whether I should just give it up and go back to nursing, but the place was too far from my home to make it a practical proposition. And yet here I was, just across the road from it and in a nursing role. The irony of it fell on me like a stone as I alighted from my vehicle. (not letting it go as you see, though I quite like "sidling", though!)

Sally was already togged up and waiting for me to do the same. Somehow, she had sensed my curiosity about the building complex opposite. She looked over to it. "That's Holmcroft Court," she said. They look after people with special needs. I've done a few shifts myself there. The gent we're going to see now, Peter, used to run the place but his girls have taken it over now." Then she did that looking down thing again. This place, and these people were clearly a bit special to her and I obviously wondered why.

I togged up and Sally knocked. She didn't wait for someone to open the door, but instead just walked in and said "Hello, ladies. It's me, it's the evening call!"

A lady in her late sixties or early seventies appeared. She had a genuine welcoming smile, a smile that shouted out a certain familiarity. "Hello Sally" she said and entirely against all the social distancing rules that applied at the time, she threw her arms around Sally and hugged her. Sally kept the embrace for a moment and then she stepped back. The lady looked at her and said, "I'm glad it's you tonight, Sally. I honestly don't think he'll be here in the morning."

Sally nodded. "I know Patricia. It's been a while coming but we're here now. It might be tonight but it's a difficult call. How's Gracie and how's the baby?"

The lady took a on a serious look. "The baby's doing fine but Gracie's taking it a bit harder now; it's her Dad after all. They were so close."

I might not even have existed for all the attention they paid me, understandably so, until Sally bounced out of herself and said, "Oh I'm sorry. This is Jason. He's new to the team." Then she looked at me with something of a humorously evil glint in her eyes. "He seems alright but we're just running him in for now."

I shook my head in laughable despair "Thanks Sally!" I looked at the lady. "They employ me for the heavy lifting I think," I said and left it there.

Patricia laughed. "I'm sure you do more than that Jason. They told us that we had a male carer coming. If you do shaving, that would be a thing, we've tried to keep the stubble down but it's not really our area of expertise I'm afraid."

If this were to have been Peter's last night on the earth, I'm not sure that he would have overly cared about being smooth chinned but then that the point, was it "Does Peter prefer a wet shave or an electric I asked. "I'm better at wet shaving to be honest."

Sally jumped in "He wet shaves, so you're in luck. I'll go and get the bowl and razor and we'll see how you do!" She bustled off to get everything that we needed for which I was grateful for that as I realised that in Sally's eyes, I was still being run in. After all, it seemed like she knew where everything was and I hate to look like I don't have a clue what I am doing, which is often the case!

I was beginning to wonder if Sally was going to test me on everything I had to do, but shaving was a doddle for me. I had in the past spent fifteen years in institutions of one sort or another, looking after patients who for one reason or other couldn't do for themselves.

As she left the room Patricia, unexpectedly hooked me through the arm and led me into the lounge where her son Peter lay in his profiling bed barely breathing. "Any friend of Sally's is a friend of ours and she seems to like you. Gracie will be down shortly with Evie." She said, "Has Sally told you about Peter?" I was a bit confused by her familiarity, but it didn't seem out of place. Patricia had an air of confidence about her, borne not just out of years of life but also out of her obvious experience of quickly making strangers welcome, She was able to feel comfortable enough in the presence of a complete stranger, like me to chat with an easy familiarity.

I shook my head "Not really. I get from the notes that he has CA lungs with mets and complications but other than that not much." Then I looked back at where Sally had disappeared to and said quietly, "I get the impression that she is very fond of Peter and all of you here though."

Patricia went around to the other side of Peter's bed which was set in a very well but not ostentatiously furnished room that I was guessing had previously been the lounge. She looked down at her son. "Sally used to work for Peter across the road as an agency nurse years ago. She was a great asset to the place, and she had a habit of keeping the staff and Peter on his toes, so it's hard for her to see my boy" and here she did that taking a deep breath thing to keep herself from getting too emotional, then letting it out slowly. "It's hard for her to see Peter on his final journey." The tears welled in her eyes but didn't fall. I could see that she was carrying a lot right now but also that she was the type of lady who would always be the glue that held a family together.

I looked down at Peter properly for the first time. He was gaunt: the cancer had clearly taken its toll slowly over of time and he lay inert and unresponsive, his breathing shallow and his skin with a slightly yellow tinge. I was guessing that he also had metastasis of the liver as he appeared a little jaundiced. From a layman's perspective, he looked very much like someone who really didn't have long. I looked up at his mother and said, "Not easy for you either, I'm sure?" As I said that, she took another deep breath and smiled at me. For sure this was a matriarch holding it together for everyone.

Sally came into the room with a bowl of hot water, a shaving set and with towels draped over her arms. It struck me oddly that waiters had the same ability to carry more than an octopus could manage. I almost rushed to her aid "Here, let me!" I said as I relieved her of the heavy bowl of water. "How about I shave Peter first, change the water and then we do the rest. Saves having bits of hairy stubble in the water, eh? Wouldn't want him to feel itchy eh."

Sally crinkled her eyes again at me this time in a real friendly way "Yes Jason. Good idea. You get on with that and I'll just check the notes." And she sat down to do just that as I went about the business of getting ready to shave Peter. As we set about our tasks Gracie came in holding her baby. Naturally, I looked up and smiled.

Gracie sat down next to the bed with the nipper. I said hello and asked about the baby. Boy or girl? Are you getting much sleep? Does she sleep through? Is she feeding well? Blimey! the price of nappies! Are you using disposables? We found them easier than Terries. Suddenly I realise that we were both chatting away about Peter's granddaughter in a room which also held Peter, Peter's mother, Peter's daughter, and Patricia's great granddaughter, all of whom were waiting for Peter to die. A huge emotional maths calculation span through my head: four generations of the family were in the room here, one of which would be leaving it soon.

Here was I, shaving a guy in a family whose mother was losing a son, a son whose daughter was losing her father and a baby who was losing her grandfather: four generations in one room saying goodbye to each other as they had all just recently said hello to the newest member. I glanced around the room at the richness of the family photographs and the memorabilia it contained. I realised that I was with them all in the eye of their storm of loss. I took a deep breath, filed that thought for later and tried to give Peter the best shave that I could have ever given anyone.

When I was done, I took the bowl myself to the bathroom to empty it whilst Sally chatted with the three other generations. Part of me felt that I had accidentally intruded upon a hugely important private moment for Sally and this family, but another part of me felt privileged to part of it right here, right now.

When I was done, I went back into the lounge with a clean bowl of water Sally and I began the ritual of washing Peter down starting with his face, moving onto his hands and then his arms. We asked if Patricia if she would like us to put a clean top onto Peter, but she declined; and we were glad not to have to pull this man around anymore than we needed to So we all chatted as we slowly washed him.

We talked about how Peter had been obsessed with making sure that every resident of the care home opposite was cared for in the best way possible. We talked about the past and we talked about the future and how they would tell Peter's granddaughter what an amazing person Peter had been. We talked about how annoying the current round of roadworks in the village were right now. All that as we washed Peter down and made him comfortable for what was possibly going to be our last visit but for the laying out of Peter's body. Through it all, Sally told Peter at every turn exactly what we were going to do next.

***

At this point I'm going to jump out from the narrative again as I remember what I'm writing. about for a moment as the writer who is writing and remembering this. Looking back, I have to say that I am amazed at how that family handled that moment and I was so impressed by their dignity and the strength of emotion that they displayed. I couldn't have really understood at the time what they were going through but in retrospect they were the epitome of how we should love each other, value each other, and eventually grieve for each other. It also struck me that if you don't have family, you might yet still be lucky enough to have the Hospice carers and they will care deeply for each one of us. That is a family I will remember and value for the rest of my life though I met them only once. Right no more jumping out, let's get on with it.

***

When we'd finished and had made Peter as comfortable as we could, written in the notes and put our PPE in the bin provided, we said our goodbyes. Sally giving the ladies both a hug, rendering the whole business of wearing PPE entirely pointless. I smiled to myself at the headmistresses slight erring. Sally and I met outside to discuss the next patient we were to visit which was Ed's dad, Ray.

As we stood by my car I said "I see what you mean about tricky. How long have you known the family?"

Sally got her phone out and started writing up her notes in it. "I've known Peter for years on and off but the rest of the family, just the last couple of weeks, just since we were called out to see to Peter." I thought to myself that it must happen from time to time, particularly in a small area like ours, that you'll come to see out of this world that you have known. It has since happened to me a couple of times since then and, strange as it seems, it feels like an honour to be there helping out at the last.

Sally looked up at me from her phone she said. "It's hard on them all but it's our job to bring comfort and smiles when we can." A kind and insightful thought from someone who was stern, I thought. "You've been to Ray already I hear?"

THIRD PM VISIT

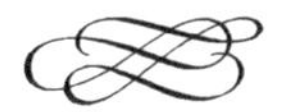

ED'S STORY

I was about to agree when I noticed that the exhaust pipe on her car was hanging unusually low. I bent down to take a look and then I said "Yes. I'm no expert but I don't think that Ray's not long for this world." I stood up. "Ray's not in pain but I'm not so sure about Ed."

Sally looked at me and said "No, you're right there; he's finding it very hard, bless him. What were you looking at under my car?" She bent down to have a look.

I bent down again with her. "Your exhaust looks to be not long for this world either. Where did you get this car?" We stood up. "I tell you what, I'll follow you slowly to Ray's and if you exhaust drops off, I'll be able to stop anyone from driving over it okay?"

Sally was seething. "This car is going back to the bloody dealer first thing tomorrow morning and someone is going to get an earful I can tell you!" She looked again at the exhaust pipe. "I specifically told them that I needed a reliable car because of the job that I do, and this thing has been nothing but trouble ever since I bought it!"

She opened the passenger side door and climbed in, muttering under her breath. "I'll see you there" I heard her say in a muffled grumbly voice from inside her car. I followed her cautiously in my own car. Tomorrow was going to be a dark day in the dealership for someone that was for sure!

Thankfully, we arrived at Ray's house with Sally's car still more or less intact. Once again, we alighted from our vehicles. Still making me smile that phrase! I could see that Sally wasn't happy. She had clearly been fuming about the motor. "I paid good money for this car and it's a pile of junk. I can see that now. Just wait until I get it to the garage in the morning. I'm definitely demanding my money back, you see if I don't. Bloody sharks." She said as she opened her boot and started togging up. "Trying to take advantage of my good nature, that's what they've been doing all along, well not any longer. I'm taking this back and if they don't give me a replacement right then and there, I shall call the police!"

Bit strong I thought to myself but okay, the car was defo a pile of crap but call the police? Might be a bit heavy handed. Still, I wasn't going to mess with Sally right now "Good idea They've definitely sold you a ringer here. How about when we've done Mabel, our last one, I follow you back to your place just to make sure you get there?" Then I followed that up with a humorous "Not stalking you though, ha!" I waited for a bantery retort, but nothing came back.

Sally stopped and looked at me for a moment. "That would be very nice of you Jason. Thank you." Then she looked back at me again. "You have your mask on backwards though. Don't know how many other HCAs I have had to tell: it's the blue on the outside." Damn! I thought. Praised and told off in the same breath!

I took my mask off and turned it the other side out as we walked over the road to Ray's house. As we approached the kitchen door, Ed was already opening it. "He's stopped breathing, I'm sure of it. Just now he stopped breathing!" Ed was in a high state of agitation and his eyes were full of tears. Sally and I looked at each other for the briefest of moments and all else faded into insignificance as we followed Ed quickly through the kitchen and into the lounge.

Sally went straight to Ray's bedside and just looked at him for a few moments. She waited a few moments more then she looked at me, nodded a brief unspoken acknowledgement and turned to Ed. "You're right Ed, I'm afraid you are right. Ray seems to have taken his last breath. It looks like he left us gently though, with your help."

Ed was beside himself, clenching his fists and looking up and out with the emotional pain of the moment: his loss. It had finally happened. After years of nursing his father it had suddenly come to an end and Ray was gone. Ed's face was contorted with grief and here I have to tell say that I have never, in the two years that I've been doing this job, seen anyone more tortured by the loss of a relative. Ed's world seemed to have just ended with the death of his father and he was clearly utterly emotionally crushed.

Sally had morphed into a different person within seconds. She was calm and her voice slowed and softened. "You've been his best friend and son Ed. How about you give him his last hug?" As she said that my heart nearly broke because that was exactly what I did for my Mum when we witnessed her last heartbeat through her nightie. Even though it had been twenty years ago, the pain of that moment came flooding back to me.

I took a deep breath and held that thought back. This was Ed's moment of grief not mine. I gritted my teeth for a moment and took another slow breath, keeping those emotions in check.

Ed nodded through his tears and walked almost reluctantly to Rays bedside as Sally put her hand on his shoulder. Then she stepped back to let him hug his Dad. He almost fell upon Ray's body and as he sobbed, his whole body shook. We just stood back and waited saying nothing This was a moment that needed no words. Ed needed to sob out the loss, the loss not just of losing his Dad but of what he had been doing for his Dad for the last few years of his life which was keeping him alive.

I knew that the next few moments were emotionally crucial, but Sally was way ahead of me. She put her arm round Ed's shoulders. "Ray told me once that he couldn't have had a more caring son than you Ed and that he was so very proud of you for helping him. He thought the world of you, Ed. You did the best ever thing for him in helping him go quietly and comfortably. Do you know that, Ed?"

Ed's sobbing quickened as he took that in. Then after several moments, he slowed, and he dragged himself off his father's corpse. Then turned to Sally, wiping his tears but staring at her. "He said that?"

Sally hugged him and said "Yes, he said that, Ed. Now take a few moments for yourself and then maybe you should phone the others to let them know what has happened. There's no rush now is there. Jason and I will make your Dad clean and comfortable whilst you do that. Has he got some favourite clothes that he would like to be seen in before they get here?" Ed nodded "Could you get those for us while we wash your dad down and straighten him out a bit?" Again, Ed nodded, and he left us to do our thing. When he was out of earshot, Sally became business-like again. She looked at me "Have you actually ever done this before, ever laid someone out?"

In that weird and very emotional moment that question made me smile. I had laid out my first cadaver / body when I was just fourteen years old. As I've said my mother was a Matron in an old people's home and we lived on site. When we / she was short staffed we had to help out. It was a weird childhood for sure: at that age and on a daily basis I was doing toilet rounds and calling bingo for the more sentient. At the age of fifty eight death is no longer a stranger to me but in answer to her question then I nodded. "Yeah, once or twice". I had done a fair bit laying out a lot in the intervening years, so I had this one covered. "I've done a few in the past but I know that things change so please feel free to lead. I'll go and get the bowl, shall I?"

Sally smiled at me this time properly. I think that then she realised that on a certain level I was okay with this stuff. After all this isn't a job everyone can do or would want to do but I think she understood that although I hadn't been in the game for a while, I still knew what it was about and what needed to be done. I think in that moment I moved in her mind from acolyte to sub-equal. (Never an equal to Sally of course but at least a passable sub-equal) That though was in her smile as she nodded to me from across the bed.

Over the next few weeks of working together on and off, we got to know each other and the journeys we had travelled to end up here in this incredibly caring team. For myself, I learned not only why they called her the headmistress but also how well she knew her job and how people felt these emotionally charged times. Sally is awesome. Sally is the headmistress!

Right here right now though, we had a job to do. Ed was in quite some distress. I came back into the room with a bowl of hot water thinking to myself, this probably doesn't need to be hot water anymore, does it? But hey ho, let's go!

We removed Ray's clothes and washed him gently from head to toe. All the time, Sally still told him everything that we were about to do despite him being no longer with us and she kept a towel over his private parts. Who knows when our consciousness finally goes after death, but Sally was always going to assume that she could still be heard right up until the last. She was as gentle with him as a lifeless body as she had been with him when he was alive not twenty minutes ago.

Ed came back into the room with Ray's favourite shirt and trousers and after handing them to Sally, picked up his mobile and rang his brother, then Babs and some other people as we dressed Ray. Ed was tearful and still stressed but calmer now.

Sally looked at me when we had re-dressed Ray and were satisfied with how he looked. "I should have called this in immediately but…." I got what she meant; things happened so fast that we found ourselves just reacting to the situation and managing it as we went but someone from the office had to come out and verify the death. She pulled out her mobile and phoned in. While the two of them were on their mobiles, I picked up the bowl and cleared everything away ready for the relatives to come to Ed's aid and to say their goodbyes to Ray.

It didn't take long for them to arrive as none of them lived that far away. At times like these, I guess most people outside of the immediate event are just in a weird hold situation waiting to step in when notified and needed.

I went into the kitchen where Sally was finishing writing up her notes. I countersigned her entries. Once people started coming in and passed through the kitchen to say their goodbyes to Ray in the lounge, they came back to us filling up the kitchen as we waited for a trained OW Staff Nurse to come out and verify the death.

A lot of things were happening, both very slowly and oddly very quickly, here was I, a stranger to them all except James and Ed, standing in their dad's kitchen in one of the most delicate and difficult times of their lives and to be honest, it was very odd for me. I just sort of retreated into the area where the herbs were kept and I watched them chat with Sally about Ray and their memories and stuff.

I think it would have been odd for anyone. I certainly felt like an intruder in this kitchen of grieving relatives who were crying and laughing and sharing memories. Yet even then Ed of all people seemed to sense my aloneness in this moment. Through his grief he caught my eye and threw me a lifeline to relieve me of my discomfort. "James did it." he said, perhaps more loudly than he meant to.

The room went quiet for a moment. The whole thing caught me off-guard and an imaginary murder plot skittered briefly through my brain. Surely, he didn't mean that James had killed Ray? and I replied, "Did what sorry Ed?" As I spoke the whole kitchen of relatives and Sally turned to look at me. I felt was in a very odd, cringy spotlight.

Ed looked down, still utterly miserable and dejected. "He did the kitchen. Dad always wanted a new Kitchen and James finished it last week. James did the kitchen and Dad got to see it finished last week." Then his face screwed up as a fresh wave of emotion hit him.

I was at a briefly at a loss before remembering that I had said something about the kitchen on our last visit. I'm an obsessive cook and I love a well laid out kitchen, but that had just been a conversation starter; I hadn't realised that Ed had hoisted that in. Then James walked over to his brother who was now staring out of the kitchen window, his body tensed up with grief; and in the silence of the room, he put his arm around his little brother, paused and said, "We did it together though Ed, didn't we? I couldn't have done all of this without you, and Dad was so proud of us both wasn't he?"

Ed didn't say anything. He just turned into his brother's embrace and the tears fell as they hugged each other. James smiled at me through his own tears, but he spoke to Ed. "You've been amazing these last few years Ed. You were Dad's best friend, you looked after him so well, you've been totally amazing"

Ed glanced at me long enough to say "Dad loved to cook, he was a great cook."

I looked around the room to see everyone was still looking at me "I can see that Ed. This is a great kitchen which is why I asked. I love to cook as well and you have both created an amazing kitchen!"

Babs jumped in "Do you remember the Chinese crisp that Dad made for us two years ago? How amazing was that?"

Then one of the granddaughters joined in: "The one with all those different Chinese dishes pressed together between two sheets of filo pastry? Yeah, that was awesome!"

The kitchen came alive again with everyone talking about Ray's love of food and cooking and this time I was part of the conversation. James gave Ed a squeeze and let him go as they both joined in the discussion. I've got to say that it was an amazing honour to be a part of that moment which I guess was a rite of passage for them all. Tears fell from all of them had tears fall and they all comforted each other.

The doorbell went Sally answered it and let Francis from the OW in. We hadn't met but I knew the form. When someone passes the death must be confirmed by a Registered Nurse or Doctor. Both Sally and I were only HCA's, so a Registered Nurse from the outside ward office had to come out. Francis was the perfect person to for the job. Her experience, friendliness and competence were evident from the moment she came into the house. I watched her as her eyes took in the grieving but laughing and smiling family group, assessing her best approach.

She smiled her way into the kitchen. "Sorry, everyone but would you mind just showing me where I should be heading?" Sally looked over to Ed and James and her eyes told Francis where to go

FRANCIS'S TESTIMONIAL

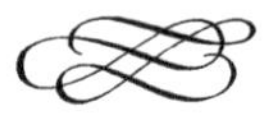

My nursing career over the last twenty-five years has involved working within palliative care. I started in the hospital working on the oncology ward. Then I moved to the oncology out-patient clinics and clinical research trials for metastatic cancer patients until I moved into community nursing five years ago. People often ask how I can enjoy my job because of what the role entails. The answer to this question is that in the worst time of someone's life, we offer advice and support to the patients and their families and we make it possible for them to spend their final days with their loved ones.

We aim to keep them at home in their preferred place of care and to avoid them having to go into hospital unnecessarily. Some patients don't have any family so being there to hold their hand when they take their final breath is a comfort to both the patient and us as professionals. I am passionate about my job and I get satisfaction from the fact that we make a difference to so many people at the end of their lives.

THIRD PM VISIT

PART II

James put his hand on Ed's shoulder. "We have to do this bit bruv. You okay with that?"

Ed nodded reluctantly aa he left the room with Sally, Francis and James. They went into the lounge to verify Ray's passing officially.

As you know, this was my first day in a fairly weird job with this team of carers, and I was still like rabbit in the headlights. I mean this is a seriously specialised area of care so in light of my near complete inexperience, I fell back to the safe ground of chatting with those relatives who were left in the kitchen, empathising where I could and smiling with them as they shared their memories of Ray, their father, Grandfather and friend.

The granddaughters were roughly the same age as my daughters age so I was able to connect with them a bit, checking out how hard they were finding their preparatory mock exams (mocks) at school and, ridiculously corny I know, but how, though their school food wasn't actually that bad their grandfather's food had been way better. (I was glad to hear a punt for home cooking!)

Eventually Ed, James, Sally and Francis emerged from the lounge saying that the local funeral directors would be around soon to collect

Ray's body, that a viewing of his body would be arranged for them all before the funeral and other important details.

Then the three of us were standing outside Ray's house. Sally talked to Francis about the event but also, because for us health professionals the world goes on, about the pandemic of Covid, how the yearly Manual Handling course was due and so on. I looked at Francis and quietly I saw a nurse who knew more about this health-care discipline than she would ever admit.

To them this was an everyday part of the job. But I had just re-visited the time, eerily I can tell you, when I said goodbye to my own Mother and watched her last heartbeat. So when Sally said, "Right; next patient is Mabel, you know Mabel don't you Jason?"

I had to jump out of the moment because a small but impossibly naive naïve part of me thought that maybe some nursing SWAT team equivalent would step in to take over from us after the emotional bombshell explosion we had just experienced, pat us on the shoulder and offer us a large gin as a reward for a job well done. No chance mate. We were the SWAT team! "Mabel, yes. She was very tired this morning when we got her up; it took an age to get her from bed to bathroom to chair. Lovely relatives I think; very caring."

Then quite abruptly Sally said "Right. See you there in five mins or so. She got into her little car from the passenger side door, slammed it shut. As she did so its wing mirror fell off. There was a pause. Francis looked at me with an evil glint of repressed laughter but still with a sympathetic eye. "Amelia told her not to go to that garage to buy a car. How is she going to finish her shift tonight with no wing mirror?"

We could both feel the steam coming out of Sally's ears as we stood there watching her look at the fallen accessory and then tap furiously away on her phone. "I didn't get a chance to say hello earlier, but hello Francis I said. Don't worry, I always keep a roll of Gaffer tape and some tie wraps in my car. We'll get to Mabel but I'm not sure Sally will be able to work tomorrow if she's depending on that heap."

Francis looked really concerned. "Amelia told her not to use that garage" she repeated "but Sally was desperate for a vehicle. You can't do this job without your own car now, can you? We can't not have Sally out there. She's one of the best."

I opened the boot of my car to retrieve the Gaffer tape. "I have only known Sally for an afternoon Francis, but I get the impression that nothing will hold her back." I found the tape under a pile of empty Asda bags and shut the boot. "She'll definitely get to Mabel's unless anything else falls off, and I'll see her home, hopefully!"

Francis put her large bag into her own car. "These ladies are a bit like a family. Watch out they don't adopt you after all you are our only male carer!" She laughed at her own joke.

I had a brief brain freeze. "Sorry. What?"

Francis looked at me slightly surprised "You're our only male carer. Did you not know that?

I shook my head slowly trying to digest that little bombshell. Then she said, "We only have three or four male nurses and carers throughout the whole Hospice so it's nice that you joined the team. Having a male around makes for a bit of a balance sort of thing and I think the team approve of you for sure. Now then. Sorry to be in a rush but the other team needs me so give my hugs to Sally!" She slid smiling into her car and left me to sort Sally out.

Odd phrase that, I thought: "You'll fit in" but I taped up the wing mirror to make it functional, slipped under the car and put some more tape around the exhaust so that it would last the night and we headed off to see Mabel. The garage was in for a storm tomorrow despite the bright cloudless spring day that had been forecast. Someone was in for a thunderclap and a lightning strike from Sally for sure!

FOURTH PM VISIT

MABEL AND MABEL'S NEIGHBOUR

Brandy was waiting for us on the doorstep of the bungalow, looking a tad distressed or maybe just wound up. I alighted from my vehicle (fist punch in the air for that one!) and Sally stepped out of her heap, both of us retrieving our PPE from the boots of our vehicles. Sally clocked Brandy's distress immediately. "Something wrong Hun? Is Mabel ok?"

Brandy looked inside the house and I noticed that her neighbour was standing on his doorstep leaning against his door and fiddling with something that wasn't there. "Mum's sort of ok but we couldn't get her out of bed this afternoon after her nap. I think she's finding it too difficult to walk now; for a small lady she's really heavy!"

Sally nodded as she looked over at the neighbour, an aged gent of around eighty years. Then looked back at Sally. "Shall we go inside and see how she is, then?"

Brandy also looked over at the neighbour. "I'm so glad you're here now," she said. Then we all went inside. I got a very clear impression that not all was well with the neighbour.

As Sally put on her apron in the hallway, she frowned at Brandy. "Have you been trying to lift her in and out of bed?"

Brandy nodded. "Yes, she says that she wants to go to the toilet but by the time we get there she doesn't want to go any more and she hasn't drunk anything since the day before yesterday anyway."

Sally smiled at Brandy in a way that I would come to know meant that she was going to lay down the law but nicely. "Maybe the time has come for a catheter, Brandy. I mean, if she's a dead weight you shouldn't be trying to get her in and out of bed. The chances are that you would do yourself a serious injury couldn't you my love and then how could you look after her?"

This is always a difficult piece of advice one to give to relatives. I have found over the last two years of doing this job that it is very much a defining moment. It's the moment when what you're really saying is that it's time to prepare for the end. The the time when the relatives have to stop trying to control events and begin to let nature take its course, however long that might be.

Brandy sighed at the suggestion and looked resigned. "I suppose you're right Sally, but I'm not sure that she'll agree to it."

Sally looked into Mabel's room to find that she seemed to be asleep "We can only ask, eh? I'm sure she'll be ok with it after a chat." Then she stopped and asked "Has he been knocking again?"

Brandy turned to the door. "Yes, and it's getting worse. We've called his relatives, but they live up north somewhere and they say that there's not much they can do to help."

I looked at Sally for an explanation. "The poor old boy's got dementia and he keeps knocking on the door, demanding food or cigarettes; he can get quite aggressive at times, quite angry."

I looked at Brandy's worried face. "Has he been referred to anyone, is anyone going in to help him?" I said.

She shook her head. "Someone came and assessed him but apparently he can still cook, hold a decent conversation, wash and dress himself and so on so they're not offering any help yet." She looked quite despondent.

This was an area with which I was very familiar, and one which I hoped had improved over the last thirty years. But it seemed not. Mental health services, the Cinderella service as it's known, was very fragmented, under-funded and under resourced back, then and still is today it seems.

If waiting lists for hospital operations stretch over years now as a result of pressures put on the NHS by the pandemic imagine how badly the mental health services are suffering. There would be no ongoing case worker for the guy next door, just crisis intervention; and a lot of people reading this book will recognise that situation.

She carried on. "He must be stuck in the past in his head somewhere because he came round with Christmas presents for us at the weekend. He got quite angry when I told him that it's springtime: he was really argumentative about it!"

And then Sally did another brilliant thing which showed how experienced she was. "Don't argue with him my lovely. If he wants to give you Christmas presents in the spring. Just say thank you. How kind, etc. If you argue with him, he'll just think you're calling him a liar. Because he believes its Christmas and for him it is Christmas. If you live with him in his little world for a while, he might not get so angry; you might even make him happy for that moment at least."

Forty years ago, they had an approach called reality Orientation. Basically you tried to convince them that your version of the world was better than theirs. It was effectively telling them that either they were wrong or they were lying. I am so glad that little boil of stupidity has been burst. If someone who has dementia is often living in the past in their mind then maybe it is just more sensible to go there with them to where they are and make them smile rather than try to bring them back to the here and now where they aren't so happy.

I had to unpick what Sally had said to Brandy later on but when I did, I realised that she found a way forward or at least a chance for a way forward both for Brandy and her neighbour. Scary though she had been in the beginning of the shift I was growing a really deep respect for Sally's intuition and knowledge. We are Health Care Assistants not trained nurses (actually, I was years ago but not now) but Sally seemed to have an intuition that's not the result formal training which is instead born out of life experience and a deep feeling of responsibility towards another fellow human being. Like being a Mum to the world.

Brandy smiled at Sally. "That seems like a good idea. I'll give it a go. Do you think that I should tell him I don't smoke?"

Sally laughed. "Yes, tell him that. You don't smoke: that's a true thing. Now then, how about you go and put the kettle on while Jason and I see to Mabel." Brandy nodded and went into the kitchen.

I could sense that although what Sally had given her, seemed such a small thing, in fact she had actually given her a way forward, some hope of improving her situation, something that gave her a measure of control at least. She certainly couldn't control her mother's slow deterioration; she couldn't stop her dying and neither was she trying to. But having a way forward with the neighbour problem there and right then gave her a sort of distraction from what was happening right here and right now with her mother. I went to get the bowl from the bathroom as Sally went in to chat to Mabel about maybe having a catheter inserted.

By the time I came into the room, Mabel had agreed to have a catheter and Sally was on the phone to Onepoint. I came to find out later that Onepoint is the central phoneline to the Hospice where patients or relatives could call to have any relevant problem addressed. If someone needed extra medication or were anxious about their relative they could ring Onepoint and the highly trained staff there would organise whatever was needed.

In this case it was Sally requesting a home visit by a Registered nurse (RN). Mabel opened her eyes wearily and smiled slowly at me as I put the bowl down and although we had only met once she simply said, "Jason, it's nice to see you again. Just hands and face tonight, Jason, I am very tired." She smiled at me, a relative stranger!

I could sense that she was indeed really tired, but I ran my mind back to that odd conversation I'd had with her that morning. As I put the towel under her chin, I said "I've only known Brandy for a day Mabel, but I have to say that you seem to have brought up a very bright and switched-on daughter. As a parent myself I think that you have done an amazing job as a mum. She seems quite strong, quite able to bounce back from knocks I think."

Mabel thought about that I'm sure, though I had no idea if she even remembered that odd moment of conversation, odd for me at least, we'd had that morning. I wiped her face gently with warm water and shower gel and then dried it with the towel.

I gave the flannel to Sally who had finished her phone call and started washing Mabel's hands and warming them with the flannel. I've noticed as well over the two years I've been with the OW that people who are close to death often have cold hands. Their blood seems to retreat to the more vital organs and leaving their extremities to become colder. Like cyanosis, blue fingers and toes, it's a sign that someone doesn't have long to go.

Mabel could barely stay awake and spent the rest of the visit with her eyes closed. We washed her gently and rolled her briefly to check that her pad was dry and clean, which it was. I took the bowl to the bathroom and left it washed and ready for whoever would be on the next shift in the morning. I sort of hoped that it was me because I had taken an instant liking to Mabel; I could see a person behind the patient in front of me. When I came back into the room she wasn't struggling to breathe but she was a little rattly in the chest.

I raised an eyebrow at Sally who was just finishing off tucking Mabel in and lowering the bed. "Secretions think. Maybe it's time for a syringe driver just for Glycol. What do you think? that Mabel is struggling to swallow even tiny sips."

I had a rabbit in headlights moment again. "Syringe driver? Glycol? I'm not sure that I have ever seen one in use before today, Sally. That's a general nursing thing I guess; I trained in psychiatry as you know."

Sally looked up in surprise "Oh, I thought you'd know about that. It's a pump that goes directly into the body via a subcutaneous needle but a soft plastic one that doesn't hurt. It delivers medication over a twenty-four-hour period. Very useful for times like this: Glycol helps to arrest secretions." Then she ushered me out of the room, and we began taking our aprons and gloves off.

When it was just us two in the hallway, Sally said in a hushed tone,

"When they get close to the end and they can't drink or eat, they usually can't take medication either, but with a syringe driver they can receive meds that slow down secretions in the chest. For others, but not Mabel, it means they can have pain relief and sedation to help with anxiety and agitation."

I spoke quietly as I digested that info. "Are you on in the morning?"

"No, thankfully," She said "I have to take that heap of junk back to the garage and" (here her voice began to rise with indignation) get a new car or someone's head will be rolling down the street, mark my words!"

Then Brandy appeared and the tone of Sally's voice changed dramatically back to sweetness and light. The actor in the me noted and admired it. "Mabel's asleep now but she's agreed to a catheter and the RN will be out before the end of the night to put it in place. Now remember to call Onepoint if you have any problems, ok?"

Brandy was visibly less stressed. "I don't know what we'd have done without you all Sally. You have all been so amazing. Thank you so much for everything you're doing, really."

Sally gave her easy smile to Brandy as we headed out of the door. "It's what we do my lovely. Now make sure: no more lifting. I'll ask for the RN to make an assessment for a syringe driver for Mabel, to help her feel less rattly in the chest. Is that ok?" Brandy nodded

"Lovely to have met you Brandy," I said. "Not sure I'll be here in the morning, I might be on the other run, but I hope you get a decent night's sleep. Your Mum seems like a lovely lady."

We headed to our cars and as Sally went round to the passenger side of hers, I said "That was quite a shift Sally. Is it always like this?"

Sally grinned. "It can be yes; but not always. Seems like some weeks we have to finish way after hours and sometimes early but that's the nature of the job." She looked down at her car. "You'll get used to it I daresay; you seem to fit in quite well, Jason. (There it was again! you'll fit in, again?) I'll do the handover tonight if you call us in safe, you know? Ring One point to say we've finished our shift and are home safe. I'll text you when I'm home. Is that okay?"

I was a bit flummoxed. "Yes of course, but...."

I could sense that she was enjoying my surprise. "And you'll follow me home in case this bloody thing collapses on the way, won't you?" I could see by the playful glint in her eyes that she was okay with me. it seemed I had passed some unwritten test. I almost felt the ghostly hand of Jean Brown on my shoulder aa if she were saying: "If Sally likes you then you did well, ya wee sassenach!"

I smiled at that. "Yes, Sally. I wouldn't want you to miss exacting your revenge on the garage, would I. If it craps out, I'll give you a lift home, and in the morning, you can make them pick it up, eh?"

Sally laughed cynically and got into her car. "It's not far from here," she said, and I shook my head. For sure, this had been one of the weirdest days of my life. I followed her slowly back to her place and beeped a goodbye as she signalled that she was home.

I'm not sure that I remember driving home that evening. When I got home and walked into the house my girls were still at Guides. I'd have to pick them up later that evening when they'd be full of stories and giggles. They were always a bit hyper after Guides. So it was just me and Debbie. She was washing up. "How was your first day then?" she asked.

I sat down in my chair opposite the sink and next to my computer. All I could say was "If you'd be kind enough to crack open a beer? I could do with a Scotch whiskey for sure but best leave that for tomorrow, eh?" Debbie got the point. She dried her hands and poured me a beer then she sat in her old grandfather's chair opposite me while I poured out my stories of the day to her. This had been a day that I would need to take time to unpick, to understand, but I had to be back on shift at 8 a.m. the following morning.

As I look back now on that first day, I remember Debbie saying that she had never seen me so engaged, more electric than I had been for years, so alive and buzzing with trying to understand everything I'd experienced.

I probably drank a tad more beer than I should have that night, but I was definitely ready to take on the morning shift. I had worked with two amazing ladies, and I'd met some amazing people. That night my heart had somehow sort of doubled in size.

SECOND DAY FIRST VISIT

WHO'S ON AND WHO'S OFF THE LIST?

I woke early, well earlier than I had for several years, to the rarely heard sound of the alarm clock. For years' I had either woken up at around 7.30 a.m. or, if I'd had a late one, been woken by Debbie. She was used to getting up early enough to catch the 6.40 a.m. London train after a 20-minute bus ride to the station, the very thought of which gave me the horrors even back then.

Debbie heard me muffling around upstairs and she already had coffee, an anti-cholesterol drink, orange juice and vitamin pills waiting on my desk for me. She is a love, but I was also suspicious that she wanted nothing to hamper my re-entry into the nursing profession if only for the pension.

So, it was coffee, toast, ablutions and out the door for me, having checked the handover already and made sure I had it readily available on my phone email. At about 8.p.m. the night before, I'd received a text from Hannah who told me that we would be working together tomorrow morning and would I like to meet her at Mabel's bungalow for the start of our shift. That made me smile, in just the one day I had developed a real fondness for Mabel, Brandy and Fran. The latter two had looked after Mabel for an age and were saying goodbye to her quite slowly. I hoped Mabel would still be able to talk this morning and as I was driving to our first call I mused on the fact that we spend a lifetime learning stuff and then when we die, it's all lost; well, most of it anyway.

Ray and Jenny were no longer on the list. Ray wasn't on the list obviously (RIP Ray) but Jenny? Was it also RIP Jenny? If so that meant that her daughter could at last begin the grieving process. We call it a process, but it is way more than that isn't it? It is one of the rites of passage that we all undergo in life, such as going to senior school, leaving school, hooking up with a life-long partner (or thinking that we have) and many more. As we know, rites of passage are the big moments and events that shape us emotionally as we journey through life.

Peter was also off the list (RIP Peter) which was also unsurprising. I thought at the time that his leaving would leave a real hole in that family because of the huge part he had played in it. They now had a new baby to look after, a care home to run and a grieving to manage. It was a tough call for them for sure, but they were a very close family, and I felt certain that they would weather the storm.

So, three people off the list meant that I would potentially be meeting, three new people at the end of their lives and three more families who would be going through difficult times. Three more families that the OW would be there for to ease the stress of caring for their loved ones. That felt a good, like I was a part of something special.

I liked Hannah from the off. She had been one of the nurses on my shadowing shift, she was around my height which was good for working and lifting patients; she was very direct and yet very friendly, and she had a way of not telling you that you had done something wrong but instead showing you a better way of doing it that made you learn without feeling like an idiot.

HANNAH'S TESTIMONIAL

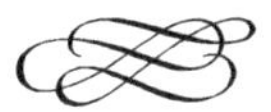

There are these moments, like when I was called in on my day off to translate. there was a Polish woman who was recently diagnosed with neck and throat cancer, and she couldn't understand what the clinical nurse specialist (CNS) was trying to say. She was crying and frustrated but I was able to interpret for her and help her to understand what was going on. She gave me such a warm hug afterwards and couldn't have been more grateful for all the help she was given. Moments like that are very special for me quite unlike any other part of my nursing experience.

Also, I've dedicated this piece to my beloved friend Shelley. She was like a sister to me. She lost her battle with ovarian cancer, and I had made a promise to myself that one day I would work for this Hospice to help people in their last days of life.

SECOND DAY FIRST VISIT

CIRCLES OF NEW EXPERIENCES AND MEMORIES

When I arrived at Mabel's bungalow, I got out of my car (I've got bored with alighting from it as you may have noticed; the police can have it back now) to see that Hannah was already there and togging up. By the time I joined her she already had her mask on and she said: "Mbl's stu aswee; I flee swo sorly for zem."

I looked at her with a confused frown and shook my head. "Sorry. What," I said. I knew she was Polish but that was an completely incomprehensible sentence particularly as it was only 8 am in the morning and not all of my brain yet had woken up to join in with the day.

She looked at me, appearing to be a little frustrated. Then pulled her mask down and spoke again. "I am already fed up with these masks! I said Mabel's such a sweetie; I feel sorry for them. Lovely to see you again, Jason. How are you liking the work?" Hannah was in her mid-thirties, blonde with a sparkle in her eyes, a ponytail and an air of friendliness and a competence that she carried round with her wherever she went.

I nodded, loving her Polish accent. It is such a musical language. "Yeah, it's only been one day, but yeah, it's okay, I think I like it; and yes, Mabel's amazing for her age," I replied.

Hannah agreed. "Yes, but have you noticed the neighbour? He's definitely in need of help, don't you think? Fran and Brandy have been worried about him for ages; clearly in the early stages of dementia."

I looked towards the house but this time he wasn't there. "We both know the score though, eh Hannah? No-one's going to step in to help until there's a crisis. Psychiatry's run on a shoestring, at least it was when I was in it and there's no money for extra training; not really effective multidisciplinary;

interventions, no real administrative cohesion, and there are always budget cuts further for one reason or another."

Hannah looked at me with a concerned expression. "Is that why you didn't come back into nursing before now?" She finished gloving up.

I smiled. "No Hannah; I was just having too much fun doing other stuff and not being a stressed-out nurse!"

Hannah laughed "Why did you come back to it now, then Jason?"

I shook my head wondering as my thought echoed hers. "I need the money of course but I'm just dipping my toes into it for now Hannah. As an HCA, I I don't have to be in charge. I sort of like that. Just helping patients without doing too much paperwork sort of appeals to me, I think."

Hannah was a little wide eyed in her agreement. "I know exactly what you mean. I love helping the patients but sometimes management in psychiatry can be...." But her sentence was cut short.

Fran appeared at the door in her dressing gown. "Do forgive me but 8 a.m. is a little early for me. Mabel has slept all night and I don't think she wants to get out of bed this morning; can't seem to rouse her at all." She shook her head in a sort of theatrical disbelief. "In fact, I'm wondering if she'll ever wake up."

Hannah took the lead. "Don't be silly, Fran. No-one wants to get up this early if they don't have to. Sorry that you're our first call. Shall we pop in and see her, my lovely? I heard that she's been quite tired." Fran nodded and ushered us through the door.

Mabel lay in her bed fast asleep, and Hannah bent over her, gently stroking her face. "Mabel," she said softly in her musical Polish accent, "Mabel, it's me Hannah. Would you like us to help you to the bathroom?" Mabel didn't stir. Hannah turned to Fran. "Maybe we could bed bath her for now and see if she wakes up a bit?" Fran got the point and nodded her assent. Nobody said it but everyone thought it: maybe Mabel wasn't ever getting up out of bed again. She might have made her last slow epic trip to the bathroom.

Hannah gave Fran a hug, and said "No signs of pain Fran; she's not been agitated at all? No breathing problems or anything?"

Fran shook her head slowly. "No, Hannah; none of that. She's been my older sister by fifteen years for all of my life and I think I'd know if she were in pain, but I don't think she is." Fran was 84; you do the maths. "She's just slowing down, I think."

I volunteered to go and get the bowl and as I turned to the bathroom Brandy came out of the kitchen and said, "Thank you Jason. I tried what you said yesterday about agreeing with everything our neighbour said and it worked so well. He hasn't been back since last night, he even seemed less angry."

I reeled back my memory quickly to replay what I might have said and then I remembered. "Can't take the credit for that one Brandy: that was Sally's advice, Sally is a wise owl for sure. But I'm glad it made a difference."

Brandy stood at the bathroom door while I filled a bowl with slightly hotter than tepid water and wrung out the two flannels. Then Brandy changed the subject like a car turning a sharp left at 30 miles an hour. "I know you can't say for sure, but how long do you think Mum has got left? I couldn't wake her this morning. She didn't respond to me at all."

I could see tears welling up in her eyes and I had yet another rabbit in headlights moment. "Honestly Brandy, I couldn't say exactly." I didn't want to risk saying the wrong thing, but I had to say something, something sort of wise and reassuring even though I really didn't feel wise or reassuring. I said, "Might be hours, might be days but I wouldn't do any meal planning for next week if I were you." Yes, I know. Not necessarily the best response but then I'd only been in the job for a day!

Brandy nodded and smiled. She wiped her eyes with her wrists. "You're new to this aren't you, Jason?"

I felt so awkward I had a head cringe. "Yeah, sorry. I only started back in nursing yesterday, I'm afraid. If it helps though I looked after my own Mum for eight years and in the last three she was bedridden." I'd filled the bowl but paused for a brief moment staring at the flannels and wondering what to say next; what to say that might be more useful to this lady who was losing her Mum and her friend by degrees. I looked her square in the eye. "I honestly don't know how long but I do know that it's hard at the end Brandy. It will be painful when it comes. But as time goes by, you'll put circles of new experiences and memories around these last moments with your Mum and over time the pain won't seem as immediate as it does now." I think I saved the moment, but I wasn't sure. I indicated towards Mabel's room with my head as I was holding the bowl with my hands. "I should...."

Brandy stood aside to let me pass but I could see that she was thinking about what I had said. "Yes, of course." she said, and I headed off to Mabel's room with bowl and towels.

When I had got there Fran had left Mabel's room to get breakfast for her and Brandy. Hannah had raised the bed up to working height and was placing a towel under Mabel's chin. Then she took the bowl from me. "So, you were a psychiatric nurse before, Jason. Where did you train?" she said as she wrung out a flannel and said to Mabel: "Just going to give your face a wash, Mabel." Mabel didn't stir.

I nodded I have come to love a Polish accent; I think because my experience is that whenever I hear a Polish accent, it is usually coming from someone usually so polite who's trying to help someone else. "Yes, I trained at the old Asylum here back in the eighties, The Asylum's gone now but that's where I cut my teeth in psychiatric nursing as it were."

Hannah's eyes lit up. "Did you work there for long? I too am a psychiatric nurse. I trained first as Midwife in Poland, then as Psychiatric nurse here in Essex. I worked in The Ponds unit for a few years.

They took in many of the old patients from the old Asylum. Maybe we know people in common?"

Have you noticed how many times the word "gently" appears in this book? It's a sort of trademark hospice is gently' I think equivalent hospital the trademark word would be 'quickly': they're under a lot more pressure in a hospital. I gently dried Mabel's face as we talked. "I moved to Peterborough and worked up there for fifteen years or so but left to look after my mother so I might know some of the older patients from my student days, though I guess the staff I knew back then will have moved on by now."

Hannah and I chatted about though we had both trained, I had let my registration lapse for personal reasons, and she hadn't, were both here now as HCA's. As we worked, we both told Mabel everything that we were going to do before we did it. I kept a hopeful eye on Mabel, hoping she might just say one more thing to me, make one more connection with; me but she didn't. We rolled her and washed her everywhere and creamed where necessary, but she didn't wake or respond in any way.

When we'd finished and agreed that she was as comfortable as we could make her, Hannah called Fran and Brandy in as I wrote up in the notes everything we had done and how Mabel was. They all three went into the kitchen. I de-gloved and de-aproned but kept my mask on. When I'd finished doing the notes, I took them into Hannah so she could countersign them. Fran and Brandy having a hug next to a table of muesli and fruity things. As Hannah signed the notes, she said "Is there anything else we can do ladies?"

Brandy shook her head "No, thank you Hannah. You people are amazing: thank you so much."

Hannah de-gowned. "You're the amazing people, my lovely. We're just here to help you get through this difficult time."

The Brandy turned to me and said out of the blue: "I like that Jason, what you said before about circles of memories: that helps quite a lot. I'll think I'll remember it."

I felt like I must have flushed a deep red, I mean I felt like a novice in this situation, but I smiled back with the confidence of knowing that what I had said had at least been true for me when my Mum died all those years ago.

As we left, Hannah took off her mask. "How do those nurses do nursing in ICU [Intensive Care Unit] wearing those masks for twelve-hour shifts, I would hate it!"

I nodded as I took my mask off and asking, "Who's next?" I asked.

SECOND DAY SECOND VISIT

THE SHORTEST MARRIAGE

Hannah leant against her car. "New patient next. The girls have been to her before though. She comes back to us now as she got better for a while and went to social care. Spanish lady or maybe Italian, not sure which, South of the town. Did you get the handover notes?"

I felt a bit bad about that. "Um, yes. But I haven't had time to read them properly yet. She's very EOL though, I think? Husband Brian looking after her, isn't he?"

Hannah just nodded. "Do you mind if we pull over on the way there Jason? I have a real thirst on and need some sparkly water. Is that ok?"

That made me smile because I thought she was going to say she needed a fag break. Back when I was in psychiatric nurse training almost everyone smoked: it was the norm.

There was also an institutional practice embedded in psychiatric nursing called 'token economy.' which skulked under the heading of 'behavioural therapy'. When you look back at it now with today's hopefully greater understanding of humanity, it would instead be called behavioural blackmail or institutional bullying.

It simply went like this: if a patient behaved well and was no trouble, they would be allowed, at a nurse's discretion, to have one of their own cigarettes (which by the way, they had already paid for out of their own money). If on the other hand, in the nurse's opinion, they had behaved badly, they didn't get a cigarette. Smoking is an addiction so to deny a patient a cigarette for spurious reasons equates in many ways to state torture. I'm hopeful that doesn't happen anymore. Some said that this control was in place as otherwise the patients would just chain smoke. Possibly true but that's why patients became institutionalised. It was because their choice was taken away from them by the institutions. That is institutionalisation. No attempt was made back then to help the patients take control of their own choices. Those decisions were made for them.

I opened my car door. "I'll follow you, so feel free to stop whenever you want."

Hannah looked relieved, "Thank you Jason I'm really gasping for a drink!" she said, then she climbed into her car. Climbed into her car? I'm going to have to find a better word than that. It's not as if she was ascending a wall for crying out loud!

Anyway, I was beginning to get the impression that this was a very close-knit group of ladies and that for now at least, I was an outsider. I got into my car ("got" is such a boring word; I'll see if I can find another before the end of the book, I promise) and followed Hannah to as she drove to a small shop where she went inside to buy a bottle of fizzy water to slake her thirst. I waited outside for her. When she came out of the shop, she came to my car to drink and chat.

We both stood leaning against my car whilst she cracked open the bottle and guzzled what my eldest daughter calls "angry water" she'll only drink tap water and she doesn't like chocolate. Probably needs therapy, I think. "How come you're not working as a Staff Nurse now?" I asked just conversationally.

Hannah took another swig. "These nurses in the Hospice looked after my best friend Shelley in her last days. They were so kind, so helpful; I wanted to be a part of that and so now I am no longer a Staff nurse but a Health Care Assistant. I still earn money, maybe not so much as before, but I love this job, this team, these ladies. How about you? You were Charge Nurse, no?"

Word travels fast in a small team, I thought lazily. Then suddenly I thought more, and my eyes widened as I realised that what she said meant that they'd been talking about me. That was a weird thought!' That was my first indication that I wasn't just joining a group of people who were doing a very unusual job, I was joining a group of people that all knew each other, probably had done for years and who were a proper team. That was in itself a pretty scary as it also meant they could collectively approve or disapprove of me. Wow! this was a weird couple of days I was having!

I put the brain fuzz in the back seat of my head and said "Fifteen years in Psychiatry from institution to personal care and all the wards in between from kids to geriatrics. Had some good times and bad, like all of us. To be honest though I thought that my nursing days were over Hannah, but here I am again and I'm sort of liking it, I think. So, tell me about our next patient."

Hannah took a final swig. "Oh Jason! You'll like our next patient, Gabriella. She has a diagnosis of brain tumour with Metastases' that have now spread to her lungs. She has maybe a week, maybe more. But she's going to marry her partner before she dies. She is very tired but she's such a strong lady. So, this morning, we do what we can for her. Gabriella and Brian will marry tomorrow, but only if she is strong enough."

Well just chuck me in at the deep end why don't you? Here I was with another ex-psychiatric nurse, the dynamics of which rumbled away in my mind for a couple of moments. I realised she would probably get my mind set more readily than a general nurse would and then the other new info she had just imparted sank in. "They're getting married. Now? That could be a tad intense. Why now I wondered?"

Hannah screwed the top back on her water bottle. "She's such a strong lady, Jason. You will see when you meet her. She is so weak physically, but her mind is so sharp. I think she wants to make sure that Brian formalises his unofficial status as grandfather to her grandsons. That's really important to her, even at this time, she's thinking of more about others than herself. See you there, ok? you follow me, yes?"

I nodded, opened my car door, and slid into my seat. Just experimenting with slid for now; don't get too used to it. I spent the next five minutes driving and wondering what this lady could be like as I drove to her house?

We pulled into a cul-de-sac with four houses in it of which Gabriella's was the oldest and largest. I parked up and togged up in the gloves, mask and gown triumvirate then joined Hannah at the front door. She didn't wait to knock but just went in. The door opened onto a resplendent lounge. No hall. Just what you would expect in a big old house and a ferocious Alsatian dog that barked as if it was going to rip us apart. Then when it saw Hannah just sat and looked at me expectantly.

As Hannah introduced me, I knelt down slowly and scratched the chest and neck of the dog whose back leg pattered on the wooden floor. Then its front legs slid forward until it was lying down. I've had twelve dogs over my lifetime and as most life-long dog owners do, I know how most dogs like to be handled. Most, but not all.

Gabriella was in a profiling bed by the large staircase. Hannah went straight to her and asked, "How are you today my lovely? Have you had a good night?" There were several other people in that huge room who I guessed were probably not blood relations. They didn't look either Spanish or Italian. As they introduced themselves the dog rolled over for a tummy scratch. Then they carried on doing what they had been doing before we came in, which was largely crocheting and tapping into their phone devices.

Gabriella responded to Hannah with a slow nod as Brian appeared from the adjoining kitchen holding a cup of coffee. He was looking quite tired and a tad worried, I thought "Not too bad last night, were you Gabriella. He said we were up a couple of times, but her breathing was a bit better." Then he bumped into the doorframe and spilt his coffee.

Gabriella looked at Brian with a cross fondness, rolled her eyes and said, "He's so clumsy, please forgive him, he's very loving but so clumsy!"

Brian smiled at her apologetically then ducked back into the kitchen before reappearing with a kitchen roll to mop up the spilt coffee. Gabriella slowly shook her head in smiling despair of him. Then she carried on talking to us. "Not too bad a night Hannah. thank you, but I am still so very tired." Then she looked at me as I approached the bed. "You are Jason. They told me I had a male carer coming."

I nodded from behind my impersonal mask. "Is that ok with you, Gabriella."

Gabriella looked directly at me, and I felt entirely bewitched! She had the dark eyes of a classic Italian or Spanish beauty, long black hair, and a weak smile. She was emaciated from her illness but those eyes and that expression on her face just shouted out to me "I'm a caring person, a tired person but still I'm in charge!' What she said was "Not a problem Jason, thank you for helping me." Her voice was slow and weak now but clearly her mind was sharp.

Hannah went to get the conventional bowl of water with its two flannels, one dark and one light whilst I raised the bed to its working height "Is that an Italian accent I hear Gabriella?"

Gabriella smiled weakly. "Yes, I am Italian but also Spanish in my heart. Good call, Jason." I could tell that though Gabriella was finding it difficult to speak, she still wanted to make this stranger in her life welcome.

I retrieved the two towels from the headboard as Hannah reappeared with the bowl. I looked at Hannah and said to Gabriella. "I only know one phrase in Italian but it's not really repeatable, I learnt it for a play I was in years ago."

Hannah gently washed Gabriella's face as Gabriella said, "You were an actor once then?"

I picked up the towel to dry her face. "Yes, I got sucked into that world for a long while. It was a play called Saturday, Sunday, Monday but it was that long ago, twenty five years I think, I forget who it was by."

Gabriella though had been processing what I had said "The play is by Eduardo de Filippo, everyone in Italy knows it. And the phrase you referred to Jason? You can't start a conversation and not finish, it can you?"

I paused for a moment as Hannah washed Gabriella's hands. She looked up at me and said, "You know she's right Jason: that is a conversation to finish. What was the phrase?"

I smiled as I dried Gabriella's hand but I felt as uncomfortable as an awkward schoolboy as I looked at her and said, "Oh, okay. *'Non fare lo stronzo.'* It means...."

Gabriella smiled and almost laughed. "'Don't talk shit.' Ha! A very important phrase to live by!"

I smiled with her "The main character had to cook an entire meal on stage during the play; the audience was salivating so badly by the end of each performance that I think we should have been paid extra by the local restaurants who were still serving at that time of night!"

I have to say only ten minutes after meeting this lady, I was completely engaged by her. As we washed her down, I looked around the room which was filled with artefacts. I don't mean dusty museum pieces, I mean parts of her and Brian's lives: books they had actually read; pieces of art that they had obviously chosen together; photographs of times they had spent together; that kind of thing. Her life was in that room as was Brian's and I thought how lucky she was to have such a family surrounding her right now.

This moment of contemplation was broken by the sound of crockery breaking in the kitchen and muted swearing. Then Brian popped his head round the door as Gabriella rolled her eyes. "What is it now Brian? What have you broken now?" She looked at Hannah. "He is so clumsy, I love him, but how clumsy he is!"

I could see Brian's discomfort as everyone in the room turned towards him although no-one other than Gabrielle was angry with him. "Just the dog's bowl darling. The dog knocked it off the side, not me this time. I'll get another one later" He grinned at Hannah. "Not the doghouse for me this time at least!"

Gabriella looked at me, but she spoke to Brian "Oh, it's the dog's fault then? always someone else's fault eh, Brian?" I wasn't sure if she was actually angry or pulling his leg. I got the impression that she could be quite stern if she wanted to be.

Then Hannah then floored me by saying, "We have the chair on order for your wedding and I hope that it will be here in time but no guarantees, right?" This wedding was actually happening and the Hospice staff were going to be there every step of the way to help where they could. That was awesome!

When we finished, Hannah took Brian aside into the little kitchen next to the main room to talk about the oncoming wedding and how the Hospice could help as I cleared away the bowl and wrote up the notes. When they returned, I noted that Brian looked a lot less worried than he had when we first arrived.

We said our goodbyes, took off the last of our PPE and stepped out of the house. As the door shut, I looked at Hannah and said, "That is one very strong-minded lady. Correct me if I'm wrong but am I right in thinking that she's the one who's been wearing the trousers in that relationship for some time?"

Hannah nodded and headed to her car. "Yes, I think so; but Brian is so caring of her. I think he's very tired and stressed but tries not to show it." I could see that.

I opened my car door. "So, who's next?"

SECOND DAY THIRD VISIT

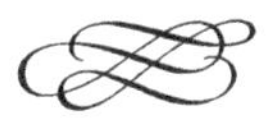

THE MUSICAL TART

Hannah didn't need to look at a list as she knew her patients so well, whereas I was just following her lead. "Mary Bremen. She lives on the coast, so it's a bit of a drive."

I took out my phone to check the postcode from the Handover notes, but I had no signal. "How about I follow you, do you know the way?"

As she got into her car "Yes, not a problem. You follow me."

It took less time than I thought to reach the next patient but when we got there Hannah didn't get out of her car straight away. I could see her looking down at her phone, probably checking her emails for notes from the Handover. I found that I now had a signal and quickly did the same so as not to look like a complete numpty.

The notes read "Mary Bremen. 85 yrs. CA mets [meaning the cancer had "metastasised" and spread] with bowel cancer. Doubly incontinent. In some distress last night so Onepoint was called by relatives. Staff Nurse attended and administered midazolam with good effect. Catheter in situ at last. Daughter and son-in-law appear distressed and tired."

I met Hannah by the door of a huge modern looking building that overlooked the sea. Both of us masked up. I said, "From the notes it doesn't look like they've had a good night, does it?"

Hannah handed me an extra pair of large gloves. "You might need these Jason; her incontinence is ongoing. The couple looking after their mum are lovely, but they're quite washed out these last few days. I'm so glad the night staff got her to have a catheter: she's so sore down below."

I took the gloves with some trepidation. Right, I thought, "ongoing" was not an encouraging word to hear but what can you do when someone is in such a bad way? I put on the gloves and pressed the communal doorbell of this block of retirement flats overlooking the sea. If I had more time, I would interview all the residents in a block like this just to get all their stories. It would make an awesome book, I'm sure. All those different life stories all ending up into the same block of retirement flats. Well, maybe one day.

I have come to understand that the thing about retirement flats is that people retire to them to enjoy the last few years of their lives and yet when they move in the last thing on their minds is the fact that this is also where they choose to end their days. One specific thing I have noted is that when building these retirement flats, the designers often fail to make the bathrooms big enough for three people and a wheelchair.

Note to self: get will and funeral plan sorted. Not got much to leave, but Y'know.

Mary's daughter and son-in-law were very much embedded in that flat: they had been there for months and were themselves retired. The individual threads of both their lives were well woven into the fabric of that flat. They were music teachers and their instruments and music paraphernalia, well ordered and abundant, were everywhere in the flat. Mary lay in asleep in her profiling bed as we entered, but even in her sleep she was a little agitated and she groaned from time to time.

Hannah tied on her apron. "Hello, my lovelies. How has our Mary been?"

Al, the son-in-law who'd been reading stood up and said, "It's been a difficult night, Hannah. We had to call the OW twice to come out and we're so sorry about that, aren't we Jane?"

His wife came out of the small adjoining kitchen. "We really don't mean to be a trouble but we're not always sure what's best for Mum do we Al? Mum wasn't responding much so they put a catheter in, and we've already emptied it once!" A catheter bag holds a litre usually sometimes three, Mary had clearly been hanging on for a while!)

Hannah went straight over to Mary, checking her forehead with her hand whilst reassuring them casually introducing me "Don't worry yourselves. This is what we are here for, this what we do. This is Jason by the way" she said as I took up my position on the other side of the bed.

I looked at them both and said hello. "I see you're both into music." I said as I looked around the room at the various instruments adorning the flat. "Do you teach Sir?" I asked Al.

"I have never knelt before the monarch to be knighted so please just call me Al," was his reply. I smiled and nodded back.

Jane reflected my smile. "We used to, but now it's more of a hobby though we still love music."

That made me smile because their enduring love of music was so clearly evidenced by presence of every kind of instrument neatly placed around the room. "Old habits die hard, eh?" I said, before cringing at my obviously inappropriate turn of phrase. I followed it up with "I used to play guitar, but I don't think I was very good. Has your mum been in any pain, she looks a little uncomfortable."

Al was the first to answer, although they were both keen to explain. "When the nurses came out to us, they cleaned Mum up but in the last hour or so she had another episode and when we tried to clean her, she was grimacing in pain. We think she's become quite sore down there from all the incontinence but at least she has a catheter now."

Since they had been so closely involved with their mother's personal care there was no question of asking them to go into the other room. I could see Mary was still grimacing even though she wasn't responding to Hannah's touch. "I'll just get the bowl, shall I?

I'm pretty sure that Hannah can help make Mary feel a little better. Is the bathroom through here?"

Jane nodded "Just through to the right there." and off I went but I could hear every word that was said. "Hannah, we're quite worried about her pain actually; it's much worse this morning."

Hannah nodded. "I can see that," and she checked the syringe driver that was hanging in an oven glove off the side of the bed "Someone's been inventive." she said as she withdrew the syringe driver box.

Jane nodded "That was Sally's idea. She said it helps stop the driver falling off the bed. Such a simple but clever idea!"

As I came back into the room Hannah looked at me with a "you'll learn a lot from Sally look" and she was right. I think Sally has a lot of tricks like that up her sleeves. She's an old hand. "I have to phone it in for approval," she said "but I can give your Mum a small injection to help ease the pain before we wash her down if you're ok with that? We need to clean her and apply creams as you know, but we don't want to distress her, do we?"

I could almost hear Jane breathe a sigh of relief as she said, "Oh, Hannah! It's so like you read our minds! Would you? That would be so good. We hate to see her suffer by being moved around and washed but we don't want her getting even more sore down there either. It's so difficult."

As I raised the bed to working height, Hannah was already on the phone to Onepoint to get permission for the jab. Normally we HCAs are not allowed to administer drugs but although Hannah was an HCA, she was still a Registered Nurse so she had special dispensation during to do so the COVID pandemic.

I put down the bowl and put the towels in place before soaking the first flannel. "How about I make a start with the flannel while Hannah sorts out the pain relief. Just hands and face though. Might make your Mum feel a little better whilst we're waiting?" Jane nodded and I began to wash Mary's face "Just going to warm your face Mary, okay?" Mary didn't respond or resist. "So, do you have a favourite instrument, Jane?" I asked conversationally.

Al, who was hovering near by looked at his wife. "Jane was and is an amazing virtuoso violin player and she's quite famous in our musical circles. She has played in so many different orchestras it would be difficult to know where to begin! I was a classical sessions musician, so I just fitted in where I was needed, really."

Jane wasn't having any of that. "He is so modest! He's done his own circuits and he's even been on telly several times."

Hannah was still waiting for approval from the staff in the Onepoint office as I finished washing and drying Mary's hands and face. I sensed that Jane and Al needed to be distracted from the immediate situation. After all, although we'd only just met, it was obvious that they'd been doing this for their Mum for quite some time, while slowly watching her deteriorate "Was Mary here much into music?" I asked whilst wringing out the flannels. I realised that when the time came for the full wash down, I was going to have to refresh the water as this was going cold.

Jane was the first to answer and she seemed grateful for the opportunity to talk other than what was going on in front, and which was dear to them. "Oh yes, she was my inspiration. She loved the piano and she played everywhere she could."

Al jumped in with a well-rehearsed retort "She called herself 'the piano tart.' She'd play for anyone anywhere... but only if the price was right!"

I laughed out loud at that. I looked down at the poor creature that she had become and said, "Mary, you have been a very talented lady it seems." Then I looked up at Jane and Al "I must say that you musicians are undervalued in my book; you bring so much joy to us all." I could see the tension in them both ease as they relaxed and dropped their shoulders.

Hannah came back to us. "So sorry for the delay but the office is very busy at the moment with so many staff off with this Covid thing. It's all good and approved so I'll give Mary an injection to help out now. The Staff Nurse will come out from OW as soon as possible to up the medications in the syringe driver to make Mary more comfortable." Immediately the three targets: pain free, anxiety free and agitation free sprang to my mind. Getting the balance of medication right was absolutely crucial at this stage.

They both looked visibly relieved and thanked Hannah profusely. Hannah pulled all of the necessary bits and pieces from her bag|: syringe, needles and sterile clinical sheet while I said, "Sorry to ask but is there any chance of a cuppa? The medication might take a few moments to kick in and I'd love to hear about your musical past. I used to run a theatre company and getting the right music for the right play was always a challenge."

They both went into host and hostess overdrive which was great for me because I didn't want to just stand around like a plank while Hannah administered the painkiller and waited for it to take effect. We ended up in the small kitchen talking about their past and Mary's past, and the view from the flat, and how wonderful and inspiring Mary had been not just to them but to so many people throughout her life.

As I listened to and joked with them, I kept an eye out from the kitchen for the nod from Hannah that she was ready for me to come back in. I had a lump in my throat as they talked to me, the stranger in front of them, about Mary. She had been such an amazing lady and she'd played all over the world. Fortunately, the old training... don't show what you are feeling, but instead help manage what they are feeling... kicked in. So, I did.

Eventually, when Hannah had administered the meds to Mary and she'd put all of gear away slowly, and noted everything down while I chatted to Jane and Al as we waited for the meds to kick in, she eventually gave me the nod.

The rest of the visit should have gone quite smoothly and mostly did. We washed Mary down and as I did so, I was conscious that I wasn't washing down a patient but a person and not only that but a person who'd brought so much joy to so many people. But just as we finished cleaning her up and making her comfortable and were about to leave, we heard a gurgle from down below!

We had no choice but to check under the covers even though the aroma already told us what had just happened. Sure enough Mary had been incontinent once again. Both Al and Jane looked at us in despair.

Hannah though responded brilliantly. "I'm so glad that happened now while the drugs are still active. If we're quick, we can clean her up again before the drugs wear off, by which time the Staff Nurse should be round again to increase her medication." Jane and Al were visibly relieved. "Just give us five minutes and we'll have her back to being comfortable again!"

Jane and Al retreated to the kitchen while Hannah and I started Mary's care from scratch: rolling her; washing her down; changing her pad, using the slide sheet to get her back up the bed whilst changing her sheet. All through this, Hannah was smiling and laughing with Mary and me though Mary remained entirely unresponsive with Hannah seeming to take all of this extra work in her stride. Right there and then, Hannah became awesome in my book.

We left Mary comfortable with and Al and Jane a lot more settled and less stressed than they had been. Having said that though, the inevitable end of the story didn't seem too far off to me. For the now though, Mary was comfortable, and her relatives had some breathing space.

We stepped out of the block of flats into a light sea breeze. I checked the emails on my phone briefly to see that the last patient of the morning lived not far from me, in the next village in fact. I re-checked the notes. Maisie Brooks 83 yrs. First visit. Referred by Renita last night. CA mets. EOL with DNAR [do not attempt resuscitation] form in situ. Lives with daughter. Small friendly dog.

I had clocked the small friendly dog in the handover before I left home. With a small dog treat in my pocket I was ready to meet the last patient of the morning and her relatives. "Okay Hannah. I'm ready for the next one. Should I follow you or would you prefer me to rely on my phone's sat nav?"

Hannah tapped away on her phone seeming not to hear me. I did that thing of waiting patiently for a response when someone is 'Phubbing' you [Phubbing, as I'm sure you'll know is what happens when someone ignores you, apparently preferring the person on the other end of their phone sort of thing. My kids are currently twelve and fifteen, which keeps me in touch with the latest lingo sort of stuff.] Eventually, Hannah looked up at me and reconnected with the here and now. "No worries, Jason. The other girls are taking on our last patient as they lost one of theirs last night. So we're done for the morning."

I had a weird moment I felt robbed. I was psyched up to do four patients and meet a small friendly dog. I know it sounds a bit odd but part of me felt let down. "Oh, okay Hannah." I said, feeling a tad disappointed. "Right then… um… where would you like to start this afternoon?"

Without pausing she swished her ponytail and headed to her car. "I think you're working with April this afternoon. I have a Doctor's appointment for one of my kids."

I was in limbo for a moment. "Nothing serious I hope?"

Hannah smiled, "Just a check-up. Nothing to worry about. It's inconvenient, but April is covering for me. You'll like April. She is very lovely."

I nodded sympathetically as I knew what it was to be parent, taxi service, carer and teacher to my girls whilst also being aware that I would also probably feature as the arch villain in whatever therapy sessions they might have in thirty years' time, possibly 10?

"Have you been booked onto many shifts, Jason?" Hannah asked.

I paused briefly, feeling a little guilty, as I opened my car boot and chucked in another disposable mask. "None booked so far Hannah. To be honest, I thought that I'd give it a few shifts before I committed to anything, um, more long term." I felt that I had been repeating this a lot.

Then she stopped briefly before getting into her car. "You should you know. It's been nice working with you Jason. I think the patients and relatives like you. I think you'll fit in just right. See you later." She got into her car and started writing up her notes up on her phone.

Strangely, I couldn't have been more chuffed. I'll fit in. Why on earth would that make me feel so good? She said, "I'll fit in just right," I thought. Then a part of me, a big part of me, smiled. You don't get much feedback when delivering cooking oil to the back of restaurants, though I always try to make my clients smile or laugh and mostly they did.

But they rarely thank me, not because they're bad people but because I'm such a small part of their very busy world. I'm there for ten maybe twenty minutes supplying, their oil, and sort of topping up a happiness catering drug, and then I'm gone.

If "I think you'll fit in just right" was beginning to sound like overworn and pre-rehearsed phrase, knowing that this time it was coming from someone who was part of a fully functional, mature working team who were clearly very protective and supportive of each other, people who really made such a real difference to so many people's lives and deaths... well that just made me feel a tiny bit awesome myself... and I smiled all the way home, still trying to figure out why on earth I was enjoying this job so much.

Then I thought about the future. This was a great job for so many reasons but was it really me? I have a touch of ADHD [attention deficit disorder] apparently. So, would the interest in the job and the passionate feelings that I had experienced over the last couple of days quickly fade quite or would they not? My mind was in a turmoil, and I really needed an afternoon nap. The nap sort of helps me to disconnect from everything and to reset.

When I drew up outside my house, my neighbour was emptying his car of shopping, they had two young kids so there was a lot of shopping. "Hiya Jason" he said in his slight Irish accent as I got out of my vehicle. "How's the new job?" I smiled to myself.

I smiled to myself not because of his question but because of his accent. His wife is French and every time I talk to them it feels like I'm on holiday somewhere else! "Jury's still out bud. But it's okay, I'm sort of enjoying it."

He shook his head and looked at me in a little confusion "That's not a job that I could do, I don't think. Not sure I could make friends with someone I knew was going to die in the next two weeks!"

I was a bit stunned by that. I hadn't actually thought about the job in that way at all. I saw it as nursing job, which was about helping people who were in need of help in one way or another. It was a nursing job that enabled me to make a living for myself and my family and that would always be the case at whatever stage of life the patient happened to be., From beginning to end, it's all nursing.

I closed the boot of my car and turned to him in some confusion. "I get that Dave, but we're mates, aren't we? I mean we're neighbours yes; but we get on okay, don't we?"

He stopped what he was doing and said "Yeah, I think so. Why do you ask?"

I wasn't sure where I was going with this, but my thoughts ran ahead of me "Well, even though we're mates, I have no idea when you might die do I? I mean you might get run over by a bus tomorrow so it's all a bit relative, isn't it?"

We both stopped as we tried to work out the dynamics of this brief conversation. We looked at each other for a weird moment until Dave said, "Yeah, I suppose so. Still, bit of a strange job, eh?"

I nodded, absently noticing that his chrysanthemums needed watering. "Your chrysanthemums need a bit of watering there, bud."

Dave looked at me and then at the flowers. "Yeah, they do though. I'll sort that out later, eh?"

We both knew that this was a conversation best had over a beer rather than a garden fence and we shuffled off into our respective houses, both of us knowing there was an odd conversation for later to be had.

Debbie was waiting for me when I went indoors. Despite working from home, she had taken time to have coffee and sugar in a cup ready to add boiling water to and a sandwich under clingfilm. "You're home earlier than I expected?" she said with the unasked question: "Did you lose one?" sitting on her raised eyebrows.

I dropped my handover sheets onto the kitchen worktop. "The other team lost one last night, so they picked up one of ours." I unwrapped the sandwich, despite it only being late morning and munched on in, giving Debbie a muffled "Thank you".

Normally she would bustle straight back to her computer and get back to being a long-distance PA but she just hung back in the kitchen and pulled a pack of crisps out of the cupboard for me. Then she hugged me and said, "I love you!"

I looked down at her suspiciously "I love you too. It's in the contract. What do you want?"

"I checked your Hospice email" she said a little guiltily.

"And?" I knew what was coming.

She smiled at me. "I just noticed that there are more shifts going later this week. I just thought that if you liked the job; and you seem to...."

I shook my head in loving despair. "I'll do this last shift this afternoon and then sleep on it, ok? I'll make a decision in the morning. I'm trying not to be impulsive [a common issue for people with ADHD I discovered later.] I don't want to take something on and then let down people because I'm bored with it."

To be honest, I still, at that time, I still wasn't 100% sure that this was for me, but I had to admit to myself that I was actually really enjoying the job and that I'd loved working with all the ladies that I had so far worked with.

Having said that, driving a forklift was a lot less complicated than this job and there was a job going at one of our local loading depots. I'd be doing something that I would find really easy.

But I knew that this HCA thing was a job that I could do but on the other hand the forklift job paid about the same, I just didn't know at that point what I'd enjoy doing more! "I'm going for an early nap, don't want to be late for the next shift, eh?" Debbie just smiled and kissed me then went back to her work.

AFTERNOON SHIFT - FIRST VISIT

Having had a good nap, I slipped on my not very flattering blue tunic, sensible trousers, and sensible shoes (I'd got used to jeans and T-shirt's for over 10 years) and went downstairs to find my eldest daughter who was surprisingly, not on her phone. "Hello, Daddy. Mummy says that you might go back into nursing. If that means you'll make money again, can I have a new phone?"

I laughed. "Haven't made my mind up yet about going back to it, and no, you aren't due an upgrade for at least a year. Don't you have homework to do?"

Her sister joined in "I need a new phone too: my screen looks like crazy paving"

The elder one held her ground "No, I'm first. I need mine more for schoolwork."

The younger one came back at her. "More like for Facetiming your boyfriend and playing Sims!"

My eldest daughter threw a mock shock look at her younger sister. "As if! At least I don't spend all my time making Minecraft cats and then killing them off!"

I hadn't really got time for this so raised my voice a little. "Enough, girls! Even if I do go back into nursing there's a shed load of bills to pay before I get around to having spare cash for phones, all right?"

My eldest changed her approach. "I think you'll make a great nurse, Daddy". Then she gave me the barb as kids do. "Unless of course you shout at your patients like you shout at us!"

I wasn't having that. "I shout at you two because of the universal rights of parents who need to keep their kids on the straight and narrow. To be fair though I wouldn't tell anyone off like I tell you off. I'm allowed to shout at you because after the umpteenth time of asking you to clean up that jumble sale of a floordrobe that we laughingly call your bedroom, you have the gall to come downstairs and complain to the house in general that you can't find your white socks and can we all look for them!"

There was a brief silence as I realised that I was shouting. "Get both of your rooms cleaned up by the time I get back tonight, and I'll put new phones on the timeline of possibilities, okay?"

They both gave me a hug and disappeared upstairs squabbling about stuff that I wasn't interested in. I went to leave the house only to hear Debbie say from the office that used to be our dining room. "You're a pushover!"

I grumped back at her "I only said it was on the timeline all right! See you later."

She nearly looked up from her computer as she said, "Have a good shift darling. Spag bol for tea tonight."

I checked the boot of the car for the necessary gear, gloves, aprons, masks, and then drove off to our first patient. April had texted me to meet her at Mabel's and had put a smiley emoji in the text. That boded well I thought. As I parked outside Mabel's house, April appeared. It was easy to identify her as she was wearing the same style tunic as mine I though it looked much better on her. She was a platinum blonde some ten or more years my junior, but as I was to find out, some twenty or more years my senior in her experience of this job.

She had the brightest of smiles a disposition to match. I later came to discover that everyone felt that April was very much the mother of the team "You must be Jason. How are you? This weather's good though, isn't it? I had my windows down all the way here tonight. Are you liking the job?"

APRIL'S TESTIMONIAL

A midwife is there at the beginning of life and it's an equal privilege to be with someone at the end. In my nursing career I always knew that I wanted to do palliative care after being a midwife and now I have the job of my dreams. Many people ask me how I can do that job; it must be so sad.

It is a total honour knowing you have made a difference in how a relative or relatives remember the last days of their loved one and for the person themselves to have their wish of dying at home fulfilled.

Believe it or not, we think of ourselves as a happy team shining a light in their darkest hour.

AFTERNOON SHIFT, FIRST VISIT

MABEL SLOWING DOWN AND SEPTUPLETS!

I immediately warmed to April and her easy manner. "I am indeed Jason, and yes, it's a strange job but I'm sort of liking it. I haven't worked with the same person twice yet though, but I guess that's part of being Bank staff."

Then she became a little more serious. "Oh, I know we've got quite a few either off sick or self-isolating at the moment. I've never known anything like it in five years or more! It's been really tough for everyone. how have you been finding it with this lockdown in place?"

We talked as we walked towards Mabel's house togging up as we went. "To be honest April, I feel a bit guilty really because despite being on the back foot financially, I've really been enjoying it! I've been able to spend more time on jogging, dog walking and cooking which I love. So, the family's happy. It's just the being skint bit that's been a bit tricky. How about you?"

April leaned in conspiratorially. "Actually, not too bad really Jason. Thanks for asking. I've been getting a bit more overtime and the extra is always a bit welcome. Now then, about Mabel. I hear she's slowed down quite a lot."

I looked around cautiously, but there was no sign of the neighbour. "Yeah. She wasn't very responsive this morning, in fact I'm a little surprised that we're here this afternoon. We washed her down in her bed this morning, I'm not sure she has long, bless her." I said that guardedly and as an amateur because as I have come to learn, the point of death is truly unpredictable.

April nodded and looked serious again. "Yes, I heard that. She is such a love too!" But that serious look disappeared like sunshine appearing suddenly from behind a dark cloud as Brandy opened the door and April smiled brightly. "Hi, Brandy! How are you, my love? How's Mabel?"

It was clear to me that April must have been helping to look after Mabel quite a lot in these last two weeks because Brandy immediately put her arms out and hugged April. "We've missed you April! Where have you been? Mum's not really with us much I'm afraid. Come on in." Then she noticed me "Nice to see you again, Jason. Come on in."

I smiled and followed April who put her bag down and went straight into Mabel's room "Hello Mabel" she said, knowing that Mabel wouldn't be saying much back. In fact, Mabel looked a little smaller since I last saw her. Now I noticed that her fingers were beginning to take on that blue tinge. "We're here to give you a little wash, my lovely."

Mabel responded not at all and had slumped down the bed looking a little crumpled. "I'll get the bowl, shall I?" I asked.

April just nodded and started raising the bed to a working height, then she turned to Brandy. "I don't think we should pull her around too much tonight, Brandy. As she doesn't seem to be in any pain, how about we just do hands and face and check her pad? When was the last time she had any fluids?"

Brandy swapped places with me whilst I went to get the bowl. "She's not had a drink for days, April. I don't think there'll be much down there. Have you been, okay? You haven't been around for nearly a week. Mum was asking after you up until a couple of days ago."

April checked the catheter and then pulled the slide sheet from its plastic wrapper. (I could hear that little sequence of events from the bathroom). "Daisy gave birth to seven little ones, Brandy and they are the cutest ever, so I've had to take a few days off to help with the feeding. We lost two but the other five are doing really well."

I re-entered the room with a look of frowning surprise on my face. I looked at April in some confusion "Seven babies! Shouldn't that be in a national newspaper or something? I've heard of quadruplets but septuplets! The poor mother must entirely exhausted and just, ouch!"

April was very kind as Brandy grinned and put her hand up to her mouth to stifle a laugh despite the serious of the moment as Mabel continued to fade. "Puppies, Jason, seven puppies. I breed dogs." I watched the look that Brandy and April exchanged.

Brandy moved aside for me as I put down the bowl with its two flannels, "Oh right, yes, obviously, puppies. I knew that" I felt like a right doorknob! But even I smiled at that though. What a plank!

Then April went back into carer mode as she focused her attention entirely on Mabel ignoring both Brandy and me as she took a flannel and washed Mabel's deeply wrinkled face. I followed her lead and dried her, then without rolling her, we checked for sores in any visible areas.

Then, in a last effort to make her more comfortable, we slowly rolled her from side to side, flattening the bed to make it easier, and slowly slid her up the bed using the slide sheet. The slide sheet is a tubular sheet made of strong nylon and when you place it under someone you can literally slide them up the bed as the material glides along itself. I might have mentioned this before, I'm still really impressed with it, can you tell?

In my mind I was thinking that this might be her last slide up the bed. Her clock seemed so close to being completely unwound and her breathing was so shallow. I couldn't help but give Mabel's hand a gentle squeeze as we finished, and I smiled to myself as I thought what a sweet lady she was and what an amazing life she must have led.

We left Brandy and Fran with a hug which was entirely unofficial but welcomed by both of them with April insisting that they should ring Onepoint at any time day or night if they were worried or even just needed a chat. Onepoint are so good at that I have found, unlike a standard emergency or advice service which usually needs to get the facts as quickly as possible, although they obviously do that too and when necessary.

Onepoint has developed to be there for the relatives as well as the patients and they can spend a lot of time on the phone calmly reassuring relatives as well as pulling in whichever particular service the relatives might need at any given time. To be a call handler for Onepoint is to be a representative at the end of the telephone of the entire Hospice.

The Hospice, like most Hospices, is a charity and it relies on donations for its funding. Each Hospice is different but the one I worked for at this time was utterly dedicated to self-improvement and continually sought ways to improve the quality of the services it offered to everyone who needed its help. All of us constantly had to complete both online and face to face learning session They are such a professional crew and light years ahead of my care experiences from thirty years ago!

As we drove away, I felt the embraces of Fran and Brandy and Somehow, I just knew that even if I had been booked for the morning shift, I wouldn't be seeing them again. They both had a chair on either side of Mabel's bed as they took it in turn to sit with her waiting, for the inevitable. I had a really strong feeling that those chairs would be empty next day as would Mabel's bed. I really didn't know how I felt about that.

AFTERNOON SHIFT, SECOND VISIT

HITMAN OR CARER?

Our next patient was Musical Mary who lived by the sea and who had the very devoted daughter and son-in-law to look after her in her final days. We drew up outside the huge block of flats overlooking the beach of which she had an amazing view, enhanced I thought by the majesty of the wind turbines that could just be seen offshore. We met by the communal door to the building. April's smile lit the way as she asked me about me and my family which in itself made me smile.

As human beings, we love to be flattered and there is no greater flattery than someone taking an interest in what you do, who you are, what you like, your achievements, your history, your family, and your hobbies. This was April all over. Someone who asks you more about yourself than they tell you about themselves is either a person with great social skills or an investigative journalist. I think April fell very much into the former category.

By the time we had entered the building, she had largely extracted from me my entire family history and my present hopes and dreams while virtually all I knew about her was that she bred dogs and had been with the OW for a long time.

She knocked gently on the door of Mary's flat which was immediately opened by Al who was in a bit of a flap "Hi April, Really glad you're here. Come on in please."

April glanced at me with a knowing look which I returned without having a clue what I should be knowing, except that there was obviously an issue.

We went in to find Jane pressed against the side of Mary's bed while Mary was restlessly trying to get her legs out of the bed. Mary was very weak but agitated within that weakness and Jane looked quite distressed. "How long has she been like this, Jane?" April asked whilst going around to the other side of the bed. I in turn stood next to Jane and slipped my arms under the bedclothes and gently hooked Mary's legs back to the centre of the bed.

Jane stood back, a little relieved I think, took a breath and said "All afternoon, we thought we ought call Onepoint but we didn't want to be any trouble. You've all be so helpful to us and Mum, but we know you're all so busy and we really...."

April cut her off whilst stroking Mary's forehead and hair "That's okay, Jane. It's always tricky to know when to ask for help, isn't it? You're doing fine and we're here now so don't worry yourself my lovely." She looked down at Mary who was obviously restless and agitated but right now had calmed down and stopped moving around her bed, perhaps as the result of hearing other voices in the room.

Jane stepped back a little further and Al put his arm around her shoulder as April said, "I think I should ring this in don't you and get someone to come out and review her medication so that she can feel a little less agitated? What do you think Jason?"

Naturally I nodded like I understood completely but clearly April was including me in the we know what we're doing club. "Definitely!" I said, then took time to have a closer look at what was actually going on.

Mary was indeed moving around the bed in quite some discomfort. Even now she was looking like a sleeper having a nightmare. If she continued to be this agitated, and as I recall, agitation comes in waves, she was in danger of falling out of bed and even ripping out her syringe driver and her catheter. Clearly, she wasn't able to respond to us as usual. All that passed through my brain in a flash, "Probably a low dose of midazolam would do the trick. Stop the agitation and relieve any pain at the same time, I think." I said.

April smiled. "I think Jason's right. It won't take much to relax her a bit. Would that be okay with you?" she said to the anxious couple as she continued stroking Mary's forehead and hair. "And we'll get the S/N to come out again and increase Mary's medication in the syringe driver, shall we?" I just grinned inside as I noted how effective April's tact had been. Jane and Al just nodded, and they both relaxed again.

April went into the kitchen to make the call as I chatted with them about music and what they would be having to eat tonight until Jane casually asked me, "How long have you been doing this kind of work, Jason?" For a tiny moment I just froze.

Looking at them both to gauge their reaction I decided to brazen it out. "Second day actually" Predictably, they looked at each other with concern. "I used to be a secret service hitman for the Government specialising in supermarket wars and assassinations. Ah, those were heady days: heady! The guns, the cars, the free ice creams, just a joy of underworld activity really!" They looked slightly horrified and then they both smiled with dawning realisation as I went on. "Actually, I trained as a Psychiatric Nurse in 1980. I practised for fifteen years before leaving the profession to become the main carer for my own Mum. Nursing seems to be in my blood." and I grinned at my own attempt at humour aimed at defusing the situation. They looked very much as though they needed more of a right here right now sort of distraction.

Al nodded sagely. "Must be like riding a bike I suppose?"

I had another inside smile as I remembered Amelia's words from yesterday. "Pretty much yes, but I'm having to learn a whole bunch of new stuff. For example, they never had these hydraulic beds before, and the slide sheet is new to me, but yeah. To be honest the ladies I'm working with are the most amazing crew, I'm learning something new from them every ten minutes."

Jane asked, "You seem very natural at this Jason; you seem to fit in quite well. Would you like a drink while you're here? Tea, coffee, or something else?" And there it was again: "Fitting in". My brain lit up as my nursing past seemed to be chasing me down.

April came back into the room "That's all sorted then. The District Nurse will be here probably before the end of our visit. Normally we never know how long they'll be but in this case it's Shirley and she's only 10 mins away. She's just finishing with another patient so we're in luck!"

I reverted to my tried and safe space. "How about I go and get the bowl so we can make a start at least?" and I headed off to the bathroom. Shirley did indeed turn up quite quickly and administered an injection of midazolam, whilst chatting with Al, Jane, April, and me before we had tucked her in for the night Mary's face had relaxed, she had settled and even her breathing was more regular.

I wouldn't see Al, Jane, or Mary again, but even now I still find myself thinking about them and how Mary the musical tart had inspired so many people. I just wish that I could have known, talked, and joked with her before she became unresponsive because from my brief conversations with Al and Jane. She sounded as though she had lived and loved life to the full!

It is such a difficult time, this time of passing, as your mind is focused entirely on the one you're saying goodbye to. And yet despite that so many relatives later take the time to write a letter of thanks. When the dust has settled, and the funeral has been and gone. Al and Jane wrote such a letter of gratitude that fairy broke my heart when I read it.

I had met some incredible people in these last few shifts. Though I have found in my later years that all people are incredible in their own ways; and I'd experienced more meaningful moments than I had in years. Seeing and speaking with people at the end of their days and their relatives is a real privilege and I get that there might be some awkward moments but on the whole, everyone that I met had made my own life a little bigger.

April and I stepped out from the flats on the seafront and breathed in the sea air, then plugged Gabriella's address into our phone sat navs. It's not that we didn't know where we were going but the sat navs tell us if there are any traffic snarl ups on the way and can redirect us to the best routes as you will no doubt all be aware.

AFTERNOON SHIFT, THIRD VISIT

GABRIELLA AND A HOUSE FULL OF STORIES

Gabriella was at the end of her life and yet within one hour of meeting her I had been struck by the extent to which she was still in charge, despite being on her last legs. I was looking forward to seeing her and Brian again. This was a very difficult and yet oddly lovely time for them: a wedding to be followed by her funeral soon after with everyone involved knowing how crazy and yet how right that was; none more so it seemed than Gabriella herself.

When we arrived, Brian was at the door waiting for us and he greeted us with a broad, welcoming smile. "Hello April, lovely to see you again." We walked into the house where Gabriella lay in her profiling bed still surrounded by Brian's relatives. "How is she?" We asked.

Brian put on his serious face. "Good but very tired now I think." We all went to her bedside, and she woke sleepily whispering "Thirsty."

Brian was straight on it. He lifted a glass of water with a bendy straw to Gabriella's mouth. She drank slowly. April appeared next to me with a bowl of water, flannels and towels without me realising that she had actually left Gabriella's bedside.

Brian stepped back to let us take care of his soon-to-be wife. April asked me to raise the bed. "Just hands and face and a quick check down below tonight, my lovely?" April asked of Gabriella who just nodded. She was becoming more tired, and talking was becoming more of an effort, but she was still with it enough to tell us what kind of care she needed in the evening.

We started the now familiar routine of hands, face, legs, then checking the pad she was wearing to make sure she was clean and comfortable for the night. April chatted to me about her previous career as a Midwife and then about her dogs and the puppies she'd bred. I knew that I should not mention to my kids the fact that I'd been working with a lady who was a dog breeder because they would absolutely want a puppy. It's not happening, not on my watch, not a chance! It's next year now and we have a puppy, damn it!

When we were done, April showed Brian and Gabriella pictures of the latest brood that she had been nurturing and we all cooed at the images. "I love dogs. Mine is a bit unruly but I love him very much. This hobby must bring you much oy, April?" Gabriella said. Then Brian asked as we were tidying away, "Would you like a drink? Tea maybe?"

We both were nearly at the end of our shift and were very grateful for the offer. "Just one sugar and milk for me if that's okay?" I said and to be honest, I was glad to be in the company of these people for a little longer. I love reading and I love stories... and here I was in a house full of stories.

Gabriella's daughter had arrived from Spain earlier and was helping out whilst telling us about Gabriella's past. Brian told us about his work and family, and the upcoming wedding and they just made us both feel very included in this so very special occasion.

I think that sometimes in the sharp face of losing our loved ones, we want to make sense of their lives. Telling their stories is one way to do that, to keep them alive, even to relative strangers as we were to this family.

We listened to Brian telling us of his and Gabriella's last fourteen years together and although Gabriella was dying, he took special pleasure in telling us all about her and her troubled but generous nature. April was all ears and encouragement as she sipped her tea, while I just smiled, nodded at the appropriate moments, and fell in love with these families, their stories and their lives for an intense twenty-five minutes.

Later on, that week, Brian sent me photos of his and Gabriella's wedding. Gabriella sat in her wedding dress in a special wheelchair holding a bright posy and Brian stood next to her with a smile as wide as the English Channel as they welded their hearts and their families together.

Another week later, Gabriella was no longer on the Handovers. I sat in silence for a while just thinking about that.

Getting married, knowing that you are dying very soon and yet still, by your actions taking care of people that you are leaving behind. Gabriella was one very special lady!

THE LAST VISIT OF TWO DAYS

THE LAST KISS

Back in the here and now, April and I were heading to our last patient of the evening. Karen Bird. Eighty-two years old with a diagnosis of CA lung. Ironically the Handover told us that the daughter had come to stay to look after her Mum in the last stages but that she was a smoker, as was Karen. However, Karen had given up smoking in the last twelve weeks!

I can't judge anyone who smokes and wouldn't want to. Not my place to do that; I smoked up until I was about 52 but I gave up because over time I started to hate having to say saying to my young girls, who were four and seven years old respectively at the time. "Don't come near me while I'm smoking." When all they wanted was to hug their Daddy.

It took me all that time to finally give up the evil weed and I haven't looked back since. I feel healthier, I run in the mornings, and I go paddle boarding with the girls at the weekend when the weather is good. I couldn't have done any of that as a smoker. Others might be able to, but I know I couldn't have. What this job has brought me to understand in so much more depth is that judging people is truly a dumb thing to do because everyone is different, and everyone has their own story.

If we were all asked to fill in a questionnaire before we were born and one of the questions was "Do you want your life to be perfect" I think we would all tick that box. I don't actually remember getting one of those questionnaires. But there you go!

Anyway, April had been to Karen's house before and she gave me the low down "Karen is in quite a bad way now. I watched her deteriorate before I took my days off over the last week and I'm not sure that she'll be with us much longer. She was very lively and funny just a week ago but when we went in to see her this morning, she'd taken a real dive, poor love. Her daughter is really caring though and distressed at the idea of her Mum finally going."

There was also a small friendly dog in the house (that always makes me smile when I read that on a Handover now!) and as we knocked on the door the dog went ballistic with barking. Bella, Karen's daughter, opened the door and the little terrier bounded out and ran around our feet barking and with its tail wagging furiously. I made a note to bring a dog treat with me next time, if there was to be a next time for me that was.

Bella admonished the dog (I love that word "admonished"!) in a well-spoken voice and shoed it back inside, apologising to us as she did so. I looked at April who grinned back from behind her mask at the irony with her being a dog breeder and all! "Not a problem for me Bella, I love dogs," I said stepping into the house.

April bent down and scratched the dog's tummy as it had rolled over onto his back "How's Karen been today, Bella?" as she stood up and started tying the plastic apron around her waist and putting on her gloves. Bella's eyes welled up and April just opened her arms and Bella fell into her embrace "Oh, come here my lovely. It's been that sort a day like that has it?" and she hugged Bella for a few moments.

I just hung back, not knowing what to say but knowing that Bella was in a tricky place, and this was a very sensitive moment. I could see the foot of the profiling bed in a room just off the lounge and I guessed that was where her Mother lay. The house was otherwise quiet, and I felt a sense of deep sadness coming from Bella.

Then my jaw dropped as she said to April through her tears, "She hasn't told a dirty joke or told me to fuck off all day. I think we're nearly at the end!" Then hugged April again and April hugged her back empathetically. "Do you think she'll last the night, tonight?"

My brain seized for a moment, and suddenly I was back up at the yard with Jackie saying, "Those fuckers still ain't paid, the bastards!" Bella noticed me for the first time. "Hi" I said a little weakly, "I'm Jason. I'll just go and get the bowl, shall I?"

Bella stepped back from April and wiped her eyes. "I'm so sorry Jason. Yes, please feel free. It's just down the hallway to the left." I nodded and went off to start the routine as the little dog followed.

Bella stepped back from April who said, "Can't really say, Bella but she has been deteriorating quite fast this week, hasn't she? Shall we go in and see her, my lovely?"

Bella nodded and they walked into the bedroom. "You brought a male carer. Mum will like that."

I smiled to myself as I filled the bowl. It's an odd thing but nurses and carers are generally seen as female, so I have to be a little sensitive around the subject of occupational gender stereotypes. To be fair though, by the time we get to see people they have already had experience of the medical system and have become used to being treated by both male and female carers.

As I entered the room, April was already raising the profile bed and Bella had put a table next to it on which to put the bowl. I did so then retreated to the other side of the bed where I looked down at Karen. She looked was very thin and her eyes were closed. "How about we just do minimal care tonight, Bella, Y'know, hands, face, check her pad and slide her up to be a bit more comfortable. You go out and have a smoke, eh?"

Bella nodded. "Thanks April, I'm gasping for one!" she went through to the lounge to roll a fag and then disappeared into the garden to smoke it.

We washed Karen's face and hands gently as usual. Her fingers were a little blue at the tips and April chatted to me and Karen as if Karen were wide awake. "She likes a joke, does Karen. Don't you my lovely." Then turned to me. "She had us in stitches last week, she did. I said I thought she would have been a great stand-up comic in her youth."

I passed the flannel back to April and started drying Karen's hand. "What did she say to that?"

April laughed behind her hand. "She told me to eff off and that she'd make a great comic now, didn't you Karen? We're just going to check your pad, my lovely and then we'll shift you up the bed a bit, okay?" Karen opened her eyes very slightly she and nodded just a little.

We rolled back the covers. April tucked the green slide sheet along Karen's back and lifted one of her knees cautiously, looking for any signs of pain on Karen's face, whilst I placed my hand behind Karen's bottom and shoulder, and we rolled her slowly towards me.

There wasn't much room between me and the wall so I had to bend down whilst sort of cradling Karen so that April could wash behind. Then frankly the weirdest thing of the last two days happened: Karen lifted her head up and kissed me full on the cheek and then lay her head slowly back down again!

At first, I wasn't quite sure what had just happened. I looked at April who I could tell was grinning behind her mask like a Cheshire cat. I turned back to Karen "Did you just steal a kiss from me?" I asked stupidly.

I could see Karen smiling a painful but satisfied smile and she said quite slowly: "I ain't got long to go, got to get it in while I can." I looked up at April and she just shook her head still smiling.

Bella was back in the house by now and shouted through from the lounge: "Got to watch yourself around my Mum Jason. She loves the men, don't you Mum?"

April laughed. "Well, Jason is the only male on the team."

And again, my brain steam-rolled me into a surprise. "Say what, April? The only male carer? I thought that there were three or four in the Hospice?"

April looked at me confused. "Didn't they tell you? You're the only male carer that we have in the OW. We're hoping that you'll stay because we need a male carer; makes a sort of balance, doesn't it?

Some of the gents like a male carer." Then in a conspiratorial stage whisper so that Karen could hear she said, "And so do some of the ladies!"

Karen grinned with her eyes closed as we rolled her onto her back then slid her slowly up the bed. With the controls I raised the part of the bed that was under her knees which would help in some part prevent her from sliding back down the bed, but to be honest she didn't look at all restless: quite the opposite.

We tidied up. I listened to April and Bella talking while I took bowls, flannels and towels to the bathroom to reset them for the morning's routine... if there was a morning's routine that was?

April was assuring Bella that it was not only was it okay to ring Onepoint if she was worried about anything but almost compulsory. "That's what they're there for my lovely and they're there all night. If you need someone to come out then they'll get someone out to you as quickly as they can all right?"

Bella nodded and looked towards her mother's room. "I just get the feeling it'll be tonight," she whispered to us. "I just want to do what's right for her, make sure she's not in pain or distressed or anything."

April continued her Onepoint line of "Just ring them if you have any worries, okay? Promise? They might not be here in the house, but they are at the end of the phone and that's almost as good isn't it." Then she popped her head into Karen's room. "Have a good night Karen, my lovely."

I was already by the bedroom door and added "Thanks for the kiss, Karen, I'll treasure that one, you cheeky mare!"

After a few more reassurances we found ourselves outside the house and heading to our cars. "We might be back in the morning," April said, leaning into me a little. "But I don't think Karen will be here."

I stopped abruptly. "You think Bella is right? But Karen was talking to us, she kissed me!"

April opened the boot of her car. "I think that you might be her last kiss, Jason. She was sitting up and chatting yesterday, I hear, she's going down very quickly now; bless her they do sometimes you know."

I looked back at the house. "Is that why you were so strong on the Onepoint thing? You really think that it'll be tonight then?"

April stood by her car door. "You can never say for sure Jason, but I'm often not wrong these days." I noted the tactful way that she phrased that. "That's us for the night then. Have you got anymore shifts coming up?"

I stood by my open car door. "Not yet, April. To be fair, I just wanted to see how these two days went."

April nodded. "Well, I've enjoyed working with you, Jason and the patients seem to like you so if you do decide to stick with us, I think you'll fit in very well." And there it was again: "You'll fit in very well." Then she walked over to me, gave me a hug and without another word got into her car and drove off.

I stood there for a moment, then I found myself in my car with the engine running and me not going anywhere. This had been the strangest two days in my last twenty years, and I just sat there processing it all, dazed, not sure really, but eventually and inevitably, I came back to myself. I realised from the car clock that I'd sat there for a good fifteen minutes. I drove home with this one thought going through my mind: I was Karen's last Kiss. Karen, eighty-two years old, a stranger to me and she would probably not be there in the morning; and yet I had been her last kiss.

HOME

DECISION TIME

When I arrived home Debbie was upstairs running a bath for the kids. This is a task that they are entirely capable of doing for themselves, but Debbie's mothering instinct was to do it for them, so she knew it was done and they knew that their Mum cared enough to do it.

There's a fine line between setting a good example and not teaching your kids to look after themselves by pampering them but if you met our girls, you'd realise they're scarily independent: they're both Black belts in karate, both speak Mandarin, both are Guide leaders and both the play piano and so I just let Debbie get on with it. I'm home, would you like a gin?" I called up to her.

I walked into the kitchen not waiting for the obvious answer but still thinking about the last two days and frankly how intensely different it had been from my last fifteen years of happily driving around in my van on my own and keeping my customers happy. Well, most of them; some people you just can't please.

The last two days had been colourful, full of people's lives and their stories, full of different ladies embracing me into their team and teaching me the ropes, each one of the HCA's so different from each other in personality but all sharing that amazingly caring nature, that passion to make it right at the end both for those leaving us and those saying goodbye to them.

The kitchen was quiet as I poured myself a beer and then a whiskey... this was defo a Scotch whiskey night... and then I stood looking out into the back garden and laughed to myself. Forklift driver or HCA working with these ladies for this Hospice? There was simply no choice. I nodded to myself with my decision made and as I turned around to call Debbie down for her gin, I was confronted by three expectant faces.

I paused for a moment, and I savoured that moment, leant on the kitchen worktop and said, "gin's ready darling. Have you two girls finished your homework for the night?"

They all three looked at me and Debbie said, "Well? Come on. It's decision time, isn't it? There are shifts going for next week. Are you going to take them?"

I smiled, glad and grateful that I had such a supportive family and that I was in that place, that lucky place, of being loved. "Yeah, of course I am. It's in the blood." Then my two girls walked into me and hugged me, and I thought how really, truly lucky I was. Until that is my youngest said: "I'm Daddy's favourite. First pay packet I get a new phone!"

The eldest, still hugging me, scorned her sister's comments. "No chance. My upgrade is long overdue, and I need new ear buds." And then she smiled up at me with her most winning smile.

I handed Debbie her gin and said, "How about you get the Rota up on the computer so we can see what shifts are available, then?"

Debbie smiled at me and said, "Just going to give Gertie a ring and then we'll do that, shall we?"

That was that and now eighteen months later I'm still a Bank nurse for the Hospice, filling in where I can, and loving it. There are now twelve permanent HCA's on the team and I just hope and pray every month that a few of them will get sick, or be on holiday, or have to take time out for statutory training, or whatever so that I can do a few shifts now and again.

My cooking oil distribution business came back after lockdown when the restaurants came back, and it got bigger and more profitable but those two days and the subsequent shifts working in this field with those truly amazing ladies has become totally addictive. And you know what? Even if I won the lottery tomorrow, I think that I would still want to work as an HCA for this Hospice and with these ladies. I know that to many it's a strange sort of job, but for me it truly incredibly rewarding.

ABOUT THE AUTHOR

I hope that you have enjoyed this book and maybe even found it helpful, as is my intention. Before I joined this amazing team, I knew nothing significant about End-of-Life care or what help was available despite having looked after my own mother until her death in 1999.

The more people that read this book the more people might be helped to be guided through this time for themselves or their relatives and so I am asking you to help spread the word. You can do this by reviewing the book on whichever medium best suits you. For me this is not about making a profit from the book but more about helping people to understand that last piece of the jigsaw that we call life so when you have finished reading the book, please give it to someone else who may need or want to read it, or donate it to a library, a Hospice, a charity or even a phone box library.

I have created a Podcast that may help people to be more informed about what happens at the end of life and the whole subject surrounding death. It is something that you can access information from about what the end of life generally looks like for us all. It features interviews with me and professionals helping guide you through funerals, paperwork, avenues of help and more. It also features people telling their stories about being touched by the 'end of life' from carers looking after relatives to people affected by suicide and much more.

Thank you for following my experiences of other people's stories and I hope to write more in the future. https://everythingendoflife.buzzsprout.com or just type in Everything end of life into any search engine and it'll come up.

Milton Keynes UK
Ingram Content Group UK Ltd.
UKHW051100230424
441607UK00006B/64